Dear Reader

Welcome! Linda H
authors and we kn
Her stories always   tension and
her strong, believable characters grip you from
the very first page.

In this story you'll meet Anna Sharp who has just
found out she's pregnant. She's never regretted
loving powerful businessman Saxon Malone for a
minute…but their relationship has always been
very much on *his* terms. With a baby on the way
though, things are about to change…

Happy reading.

The Editors

The Way Home

LINDA HOWARD

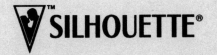

SILHOUETTE®

*Silhouette and Colophon are registered trademarks of
Harlequin Books S.A., used under licence.*

*First published in Great Britain 1993
Silhouette Books, Eton House, 18-24 Paradise Road,
Richmond, Surrey TW9 1SR*

© Linda Howington 1991

Originally published in To Mother With Love
© Silhouette Books 1991

ISBN 0 373 59655 3

54-9902

*Printed and bound in Great Britain
by Caledonian International Book Manufacturing Ltd, Glasgow*

A Note from Linda Howard

The subject of motherhood, of course, reminds me of my mother, with her common sense and good humor, both of which, with six children, she desperately needed. She was a little goofy in some things and downright eerie in others, such as the way she unerringly knew, without a shred of evidence, whenever one of us was hurt or in trouble or, unfortunately, doing our darnedest to *get* in trouble. We didn't even have to be there for her to sense when something was going wrong with us. On the other hand, sometimes she cheerfully joined in our mischief as if she were no older than we were.

Our friends from school loved to stay over at our house because of our mother. She was fun to be with and answered all of our questions, on any subject, with honesty and without embarrassment. She wasn't a good housekeeper or a particularly good cook, though she had "specialties" that were mouthwatering, but those things weren't important to either us or our friends. She was our rock.

But what makes me smile the most when I remember her isn't the things she did, but rather, the things she didn't do. Like the time she *didn't* kill me when I set the living room floor on fire. See, I was four years old and I wanted to paint a picture, but I didn't have any paint, so I decided to melt my crayons. To make a long story short, the floor caught fire before the crayons even got soft. I stomped the floor and extinguished the flames, then fetched her to show her the scorch marks and to confess what I'd been trying to do not because I was noble, but because I was highly indignant that those stupid crayons were so hard to melt and I obviously needed her help to paint my picture. Like I said, to her credit, she didn't kill me. She warned me that I was never to try that again (I didn't; after all, it obviously didn't work), and took me outside to show me how to pick poke berries and mash them up to use the purple dye for painting.

She *didn't* kill my brother Butch and me for taking the screens off the windows to use to sift dirt so we could make a really high-quality road system for our toy cars. Or for trying to dig a hole to China beneath the big oak tree, which also sheltered our road system. Actually, the hole totally escaped her notice until we missed our youngest brother, Tim, and finally traced these small cries for help to the hole to China. I remember being irritated that it was Tim instead of a little Chinese boy coming through from the other side.

She *didn't* kill Paul when he decorated the dining room with every tube of lipstick that he could find.

She *didn't* kill us when she returned from buying groceries to see, as she topped the hill, this enormous fire in the front yard. It hadn't rained in a while, so we'd decided to do a rain dance. To do a rain dance, you have to have a fire, right? Anyway, she was totally calm as she pulled into the driveway, picked up the bag of groceries and started into the house. As she passed us she casually asked, "What's the fire for?"

"We're doing a rain dance!"

"Put it out."

We put it out, and eventually, the grass grew back. It also rained the next day, to our pride.

So this is to our mother, who managed to keep her sanity despite six stubborn, brawling, inquisitive and highly unorthodox children. All of the good times are what I remember best about her.

Linda Howard

Prologue

The Beginning

Saxon Malone didn't look at her as he said, "This won't work. You can be either my secretary or my mistress, but you can't be both. Choose."

Anna Sharp paused, her nimble fingers poised in suspended animation over the stack of papers she had been sorting in search of the contract he had requested. His request had come out of the blue, and she felt as if the breath had been knocked out of her. *Choose,* he'd said. It was one or the other. Saxon always said exactly what he meant and backed up what he'd said.

In a flash of clarity she saw precisely how it would be, depending on which answer she gave. If she chose to be his secretary, he would never again make any move toward her that could be construed as personal. She knew Saxon well, knew his iron will and how completely he could compartmentalize his life. His personal life never bled over into business, or vice versa. If she chose to be his lover— no, his *mistress*—he would expect to completely support her, just as sugar daddies had traditionally done over the centuries, and in exchange she would be sexually available to him whenever he had the time or inclination to visit. She would be expected to give him total fidelity while he promised nothing in return, neither faithfulness nor a future.

Common sense and self-respect demanded that she choose the upright position of secretary as opposed to the horizontal position of mistress, yet still she hesitated. She had been Saxon's secretary for a year, and had loved him for most of that time. If she chose her job, he would never allow her to get any closer to him than she was right now. As his mistress, at least she would have the freedom to express her love in her own way and the hours spent in his arms as a talisman against a future without him, which she would eventually have to face. Saxon wasn't a staying man, one with whom a woman could plan a life. He didn't tolerate any ties.

She said, her voice low, "If I choose to be your mistress, then what?"

He finally looked up, and his dark green eyes were piercing. "Then I get a new secretary," he said flatly. "And don't expect me to ever offer marriage, because I won't. Under any circumstances."

She took a deep breath. He couldn't have stated it any plainer than that. The wildfire physical attraction that had overtaken them the night before would never become anything stronger, at least not for him. He wouldn't permit it.

She wondered how he could remain so impassive after the hours of fierce lovemaking they had shared on the very carpet beneath her feet. If it had been one hasty mating, perhaps they would have been able to ignore it as an aberration, but the fact was that they had made love over and over again in a prolonged frenzy, and there was no pretending otherwise. His office was permeated with sexual memories; he had taken her on the floor, on the couch, on the desk that was now covered with contracts and proposals; they had even made love in his washroom. He hadn't been a gentle lover; he'd been demanding, fierce, almost out of control, but generous in the way he had made certain she'd been as satisfied as he by each encounter. The thought of never again knowing that degree of passion made her heart squeeze painfully.

She was twenty-seven and had never loved before—never even, as a teenager, had the usual assortment of crushes or gone steady. If she passed up this chance she might never have another, and certainly never another with Saxon.

So, in full possession of her faculties, she took the step that would make her Saxon Malone's kept woman. "I choose to be your mistress," she said softly. "On one condition."

There was a hot flare in his deep-set eyes that just as quickly cooled at her last words. "No conditions."

"There has to be this one," she insisted. "I'm not naive enough to think this relationship—"

"It isn't a relationship. It's an arrangement."

"—this *arrangement* will last forever. I want to have the security of supporting myself, earning my own way, so I won't suddenly find myself without a place to live or the means of making a living."

"*I'll* support you, and believe me, you'll earn every penny of it," he said, his eyes moving down her body in a way that made her feel suddenly naked, her flesh too hot and too tight. "I'll set up a stock portfolio for you, but I don't want you working, and that's final."

She hated it that he would put their relationship— for it *was* a relationship, despite his insistence to the contrary—on such a mercenary basis, but she knew it was the only basis he could agree to. She, on the other hand, would take him on any basis he desired.

"All right," she said, automatically searching for the words he could accept and understand, words that lacked any hint of emotion. "It's a deal."

He stared at her in silence for a long minute, his face as unreadable as usual. Only the heat in his eyes gave him away. Then he rose deliberately to his feet and walked to the door, which he closed and locked, even though it was after quitting time and they were alone. When he turned back to her, Anna could plainly see his arousal, and her entire body tightened in response. Her breath was already coming fast and shallow as he reached for her.

"Then you might as well begin now," he said, and drew her to him.

Chapter One

Two years later

Anna heard his key in the door and sat up straight on the sofa, her heart suddenly beating faster. He was back a day earlier than he'd told her, and of course he hadn't called; he never called her when he was gone on a trip, because that would be too much like acknowledging a relationship, just as he insisted, even after two years, on maintaining separate residences. He still had to go home every morning to change clothes before he went to work.

She didn't jump up to run into his arms; that, too, was something that would make him uncomfortable. By now, she knew the man she loved very well. He couldn't accept anything that resembled caring, though she didn't know why. He was very careful never to appear to be rushing to see her; he never called her by a pet name, never gave her any fleeting, casual caresses, never whispered love words to her even during the most intense lovemaking. What he said to her in bed were always words of sexual need and excitement, his voice guttural with tension, but he was a sensual, giving lover. She loved making love with him, not only because of the satisfaction he always gave her, but because under the guise of physical desire she was able to give him all the affection he couldn't accept outside of bed.

When they were making love she had a reason for touching him, kissing him, holding him close, and during those moments he was free with his own caresses. During the long, dark nights he was insatiable, not just for sex but for the closeness of her; she slept every night in his arms, and if for some reason she moved away from him during the night he would wake and reach for her, settling her against him once more. Come morning, he would withdraw back into his solitary shell, but during the nights he was completely hers. Sometimes she felt that he needed the nights as intensely as she did, and for the same reasons. They were the only times when he allowed himself to give and accept love in any form.

So she forced herself to sit still, and kept the book she'd been reading open on her lap. It wasn't until the door had opened and she heard the thump of his suitcase hitting the floor that she allowed herself to look up and smile. Her heart leaped at the first sight of him, just as it had been doing for three years, and pain squeezed her insides at the thought of never seeing him again. She had one more night with him, one more chance, and then she would have to end it.

He looked tired; there were dark shadows under his eyes, and the grooves bracketing his beautiful mouth were deeper. Even so, not for the first time, she was struck by how incredibly good-looking he was, with his olive-toned skin, dark hair and the pure, dark green of his eyes. He had never mentioned his parents, and now she wondered about them, about the combination of genes that had produced such striking coloring, but that was another thing she couldn't ask.

He took off his suit jacket and hung it neatly in the closet, and while he was doing that, Anna went over to the small bar and poured him two fingers of Scotch, neat. He took the drink from her with a sigh of appreciation, and sipped it while he began loosening the knot of his tie. Anna stepped back, not wanting to crowd him, but her eyes lingered on his wide, muscled chest, and her body began to quicken in that familiar way.

"Did the trip go all right?" she asked. Business was always a safe topic.

"Yeah. Carlucci was overextended, just like you said." He finished the drink with a quick toss of his wrist, then set the glass aside and put his hands on her waist. Anna tilted her head back, surprise in her eyes. What was he doing? He always followed a pattern when he returned from a trip: he would shower while she prepared a light meal; they would eat; he would read the newspaper, or they would talk about his trip; and finally they would go to bed. Only then would he unleash his sensuality, and they would make love for hours. He had done that for two years, so why was he breaking his own pattern by reaching for her almost as soon as he was in the door?

She couldn't read the expression in his green eyes; they were too shuttered, but were glittering oddly. His fingers bit into her waist.

"Is something wrong?" she asked, anxiety creeping into her tone.

He gave a harsh, strained laugh. "No, nothing's wrong. It was a bitch of a trip, that's all." Even as he spoke, he was moving them toward the bedroom. Once there, he turned her around and began undressing her, pulling at her clothes in his impatience. She stood docilely, her gaze locked on his face. Was it her imagination, or did a flicker of relief cross his face when at last she was nude and he pulled her against him? He wrapped his arms tightly around her, almost crushing her. His shirt buttons dug into her breasts, and she squirmed a little, docility giving way to a growing arousal. Her response to him was always strong and immediate, rising to meet his.

She tugged at his shirt. "Don't you think you'd be better off without this?" she whispered. "And this?" She slipped her hands between them and began unbuckling his belt.

He was breathing harder, his body heat burning

her even through his clothes. Instead of stepping
back so he could undress, he tightened his arms
around her and lifted her off her feet, then carried
her to the bed. He let himself fall backward, with
her still in his arms, then rolled so that she was
beneath him. She made a tight little sound in her
throat when he used his muscular thigh to spread
her legs, and his hips settled into the notch he'd just
made.

"Anna." Her name was a groan coming from
deep in his chest. He caught her face between his
hands and ground his mouth against hers, then
reached down between their bodies to open his
pants. He was in a frenzy, and she didn't know why,
but she sensed his desperate need of her and held
herself still for him. He entered her with a heavy
surge that made her arch off the bed. She wasn't
ready, and his entry was painful, but she pushed her
fingers into his hair and clasped his head, trying to
give him what comfort she could, though she didn't
know what was wrong.

Once he was inside her, however, the desperation
faded from his eyes and she felt the tension in his
muscles subside. He sank against her with a muted
groan of pleasure, his heavy weight crushing her
into the bed. After a moment he propped himself on
his elbows. "I'm sorry," he whispered. "I didn't
mean to hurt you."

She gave him a gentle smile and smoothed his

hair. "I know," she replied, applying pressure to his head to force him down within kissing range. Her body had accustomed itself to him, and the pain of his rough entry was gone, leaving only the almost incandescent joy of making love with him. She had never said it aloud, but her body said it, and she always echoed it in her mind: *I love you.* She said the inner words again as he began moving, and she wondered if it would be for the last time.

Later, she woke from a light doze to hear the shower running. She knew she should get up and begin preparations for a meal, but she was caught in a strange inertia. She couldn't care about food when the rest of her life depended on what happened between them now. She couldn't put it off any longer.

Maybe tonight *wouldn't* be the last time. Maybe. Miracles had happened before.

She might hope for a miracle, but she was prepared for a less perfect reality. She would be moving out of this chic, comfortable apartment Saxon had provided for her. Her next living quarters wouldn't be color-coordinated, but so what? Matching carpets and curtains didn't matter. Saxon mattered, but she wouldn't be able to have him. She only hoped she would be able to keep from crying and begging; he would hate that kind of scene.

Being without him was going to be the most difficult thing she had ever faced. She loved him even more now than she had two years before, when she had agreed to be his mistress. It always squeezed her heart the way he would do something considerate, then go out of his way to make it appear as just a casual gesture that had happened to present itself, that he hadn't gone to any trouble to do something for her. And there was the concern he had shown over minor colds, the quiet way he had steadily built up an impressive stock portfolio in her name so she would be financially secure, and the way he always complimented whatever she cooked.

She had never seen anyone who needed to be loved more than Saxon, nor anyone who rejected any sign of love so fiercely.

He was almost fanatically controlled—and she adored it when his control shattered when they made love, though never before had he been as frenzied, as *needy,* as he had been tonight. Only when they were making love did she see the real Saxon, the raw passion he kept hidden the rest of the time. She cherished all of his expressions, but her most cherished image was the way he looked when they made love, his black hair damp with sweat, his eyes fierce and bright, all reserve burned away as his thrusts increased in both depth and speed.

She had no photographs of him. She would have to keep those mental images sharp and polished, so she could take them out and examine them whenever the loneliness became too intense. Later, she would painstakingly compare his beloved face with another that was equally precious, and search for the similarities that would both comfort and torment her.

She smoothed her hands over her stomach, which was still flat and revealed nothing yet of the child growing within.

She had had few symptoms to signal her pregnancy, though she was almost four months along. This last period was the first one she had skipped entirely; the first one after conception had been light, and the second one little more than heavy spotting. It was the spotting that had sent her to the doctor for a precautionary exam, which had revealed that she was in good physical condition and undoubtedly pregnant. She had had no morning sickness, only a few isolated bouts of queasiness that had held no significance except in retrospect. Her breasts were now becoming a bit tender, and she had started taking naps, but other than that she felt much as she had before. The biggest difference was in the almost overwhelming emotions she felt for this baby, Saxon's baby: delirious joy at its presence within her; fierce protectiveness; a powerful sense of physical possession; impatience to actually hold it in her arms; and an almost intolerable sense of loss, because she was terrified that she would lose the father as she gained the child.

Saxon had made it plain from the start that he would accept no strings, and a child wasn't merely a string, it was an unbreakable chain. He would find that intolerable. Just the knowledge of her pregnancy would be enough to drive him away.

She had tried to resent him, but she couldn't. She had gone into this with her eyes open; Saxon had never tried to hide anything from her, never made any promises, had in fact gone out of his way to make certain she knew he would never offer anything more than a physical relationship. He had done nothing other than what he'd said he would do. It wasn't his fault that their birth control had failed, nor was it his fault that losing him would break her heart.

The shower had stopped running. After a minute he walked naked into the bedroom, rubbing a towel over his wet hair. A small frown pulled his brows downward when he saw she was still in bed; he draped the towel around his neck and came over to sit beside her on the bed, sliding his hand under the sheet in search of her warm, pliant body. His hand settled on her belly. "Are you all right?" he asked with concern. "Are you sure I didn't hurt you?"

She put a hand over his. "I'm fine." More than fine, lying there with his hand resting over the child he had given her.

He yawned, then shrugged to loosen the muscles of his shoulders. There was no sign now of his former tension; his expression was relaxed, his eyes lazy with satisfaction. "I'm hungry. Do you want to eat in or go out for dinner?"

"Let's eat in." She didn't want to spend their last night together in the middle of a crowded restaurant.

As he started to get up, she tightened her hand on his, keeping him in place. He gave her a look of mild surprise. She took a deep breath, knowing she had to get this over with now before she lost her nerve, yet when the words came out they weren't the ones she had planned. "I've been wondering…what would you do if I happened to get pregnant?"

Like a shutter closing, his face lost all expression and his eyes frosted over. His voice was very deep and deliberate when he said, "I told you in the beginning, I won't marry you, under any circumstances, so don't try getting pregnant to force my hand. If you're looking for marriage, I'm not the man, and maybe we should dissolve our arrangement."

The tension was back, every line of his big body taut as he sat naked on the side of the bed and waited for her answer, but she could see no sign of worry in his face. He had already made his decision, and now he was waiting to hear hers. There was such a heavy weight crushing her chest that she could hardly bear it, but his answer had been no more than what she had expected.

But she found that she couldn't say the words that would make him get up, dress and walk out. Not right now. In the morning. She wanted to have this last night with him, held close in his arms. She wanted to tell him that she loved him just one more time, in the only way he would allow.

Chapter Two

Saxon woke early the next morning and lay in the dim light of dawn, unable to go back to sleep because of the echo of tension left behind by the question Anna had asked the night before. For a few nightmarish moments he had seen his entire life caving in around him, until Anna had smiled her quiet smile and said gently, "No, I'd never try to force you to marry me. It was just a question."

She was still sleeping, her head pillowed on his left shoulder, his left arm wrapped around her, his right hand resting on her hip. From the very first he hadn't been able to sleep unless she was close to him. He had slept alone his entire adult life, but when Anna had become his mistress he had abruptly found, to his surprise, that sleeping alone was almost impossible.

It was getting worse. Business trips had never bothered him before; he had, in fact, thrived on them, but lately they had been irritating the hell out of him. This last trip had been the worst yet. The delays, glitches and aggravations hadn't been anything out of the ordinary, but what he had once taken for granted now grated almost unbearably. A late flight could send him into a rage; a mislaid blueprint was almost enough to get someone fired; a broken piece of equipment had him swearing savagely; and to top it off, he hadn't been able to sleep. The hotel noises and unfamiliar bed had been particularly annoying, though he probably wouldn't have noticed them at all if Anna had been there with him. That admission alone had been enough to make him break out in a sweat, but added to it was a gnawing need to get back home to Denver, to Anna. It wasn't until he had had her beneath him in bed, until he had felt the soft warmth of her body enfold him, that he had at last been able to relax.

He had walked through the door of the apartment and desire had hit him like a blow, low down and hard. Anna had looked up with her customary smile, her dark eyes as calm and serene as a shadowy pool, and his savage mood had faded, to be replaced by pure sexual need. Walking through that door had been like walking into a sanctuary to find a woman made specifically for him. She had poured him a drink and brushed close to him, and he had smelled the sweet scent of her skin that always clung to their sheets, the scent that had been maddeningly absent from the hotel linens. The ferocity of the desire that had taken hold of him still left him a little shaken this morning.

Anna. He had noticed that serenity, and the feminine scent of her, from the very first day when he had hired her as his secretary. He had wanted her from the beginning, but had controlled his sexual urges because he had neither wanted nor needed that sort of complication on the job. Gradually, though, the wanting had grown stronger, until it had become an unbearable need that gnawed at him day and night, and his control had begun crumbling.

Anna looked like honey, and he had been going mad wanting to taste her. She had silky, light brown hair, streaked with blond, and dark-honey eyes. Even her skin had a smooth, warm, honey tone to it. She would never be flashy, but she was so pleasant to look at that people continually turned her way. And those honey eyes had always been warm and calm and inviting, until finally he had been unable to resist the invitation. The frenzy of that first night still startled him, even in memory, because he had never lost control—until then. He had lost it with Anna, deep inside her hot, honeyed depths, and sometimes he felt that he had never gotten it back.

He had never let anyone get close to him, but after that first night he had known that he couldn't walk away from her as he had from the others. Acknowledging that simple fact had terrified him. The only way he had been able to handle it had been to completely separate her from the other parts of his life. She could be his mistress, but nothing else. He couldn't let her matter too much. He still had to constantly guard against letting her get too close; Anna could destroy him, and something deep inside him knew it. No one else had ever even threatened his defenses, and there were times when he wanted to walk out and never come back, never see her again, but he couldn't. He needed her too much, and he constantly fought to keep her from realizing it.

But their arrangement made it possible for him to sleep with her every night and lose himself over and over in her warm, pliant body. In bed he could kiss her and smooth his hands over her, wrap himself in her scent and touch. In bed he could feed his craving for honey, his savage need to touch her, to hold her close. In bed she clung to him with abandon, opening herself to him whenever he wanted, her hands sliding over him in bold, tender caresses that drove him wild. Once they were in bed together, it seemed as if she never stopped touching him, and despite himself, he reveled in it. Sometimes it was all he could do to keep from groaning in a strange, not completely physical ecstasy as she petted and stroked and cuddled.

Yet for all that they had virtually lived together for two years—the small distance that he insisted on retaining, so necessary for him, was in fact negligible in terms of time—he knew little more about her now than he had before. Anna didn't bombard anyone with the details of her past or present life, and he hadn't asked, because to do so would give her the same right to question him about his own past, which was something he seldom allowed himself to even think about. He knew how old she was, where she had been born, where she had gone to school, her social security number, her former jobs, because all that had been in her personnel record. He knew that she was conscientious, good with details and preferred a quiet life. She seldom drank alcohol, and lately seemed to have stopped drinking altogether. She read quite a bit, and her interests were wide and varied in both fiction and nonfiction. He knew that she preferred pastel colors and didn't like spicy foods.

But he didn't know if she had ever been in love, what had happened to her family—in her personnel file, "None" had been listed in the next-of-kin column—if she had been a cheerleader or ever gotten into trouble for childish pranks. He didn't know why she had moved to Denver, or what her dreams were. He knew only the surface facts that were there for anyone to see, not her memories or hopes.

Sometimes he was afraid that, because he knew so little about her, she might someday slip away from him. How could he predict what she would do when he knew nothing of her thoughts and had only himself to blame? He had never asked, never encouraged her to talk to him of those parts of her life. For the past two years he had lived in quiet terror, dreading the day when he would lose her, but unable to do anything to stop it. He didn't know how to reach out to her, how to hold her, when even the thought of letting her know how vulnerable he was to her had the power to make him physically sick.

The hunger grew in him as he thought of her, felt her lying so soft against his side, and his manhood swelled in response. If they had no other form of contact, they at least had this, the almost overwhelming sexual need for each other. He had never before wanted anything from a woman except sex; it was bitterly ironic that now he was using sex to give him at least the semblance of closeness with her. His heartbeat kicked into a faster rate as he began stroking her, easing her awake and into passion so he could ease himself into her and forget, for a while, everything but the incredible pleasure of making love to her.

It was one of those sunny days when the brightness seemed almost overwhelming, the air was clear and warm for late April, a perfect day, a mockery of a day, because she felt as if her heart were dying inside of her. She cooked breakfast, and they ate it on the terrace, as they often did during good weather. She poured him another cup of coffee and sat down across from him, then folded her hands around her chilled glass of orange juice so they wouldn't shake.

"Saxon." She couldn't look at him, so she focused on the orange juice. She felt nauseated, but it was more a symptom of heavy dread than of her pregnancy.

He had been catching up on the local news, and now he looked up at her over the top of a newspaper. She felt his attention focus on her.

"I have to leave," she said in a low voice.

His face paled, and for a long minute he sat as if turned to stone, not even blinking. A slight breeze rattled the newspaper, and finally he moved, folding the pages slowly and painstakingly, as if every movement were painful. The time had come, and he didn't know if he could bear it, if he could even speak. He looked at Anna's lowered head, at the way the sun glinted on the pale, silky streaks, and knew that he had to speak. This time, at least, he wanted to know why.

So that was the question he asked, that one word, and it came out sounding rusty. "Why?"

Anna winced at the raw edge to his voice. "Something has happened. I didn't plan it. It—it just happened."

She had fallen in love with someone else, he thought, fighting to catch his breath over the knot of agony in his chest. He had always trusted her completely, had never even entertained the thought that she might be seeing other men during his absences, but obviously he'd been wrong.

"Are you leaving me for another man?" he asked harshly.

Her head jerked up, and she stared at him, stunned by the question. He looked back at her, his eyes fierce and greener than she had ever seen them before.

"No," she whispered. "Never that."

"Then what?" He shoved himself away from the table and stood, his big body taut with barely controlled rage.

She took a deep breath. "I'm pregnant."

Just for an instant his fierce expression didn't change; then all of a sudden his face turned to stone, blank and hard. "What did you say?"

"I'm pregnant. Almost four months. It's due around the end of September."

He turned his back on her and walked to the terrace wall to look out over the city. The line of his shoulders was rigid with anger. "By God, I never thought you'd do this," he said, his voice harshly controlled. "I've been suckered all the way, haven't I? I should have known what to expect after the question you asked last night. Marriage would be more profitable than a paternity suit, wouldn't it? But you stand to make a good profit either way."

Anna got up from the table and quietly walked back into the apartment. Saxon stood by the wall, his fists knotted as he tried to deal with both blind rage and the cold knot of betrayal, as well as the pain that waited, crouched and ready, to come to the fore at the least abatement of anger.

He was too tense to stand there long; when he couldn't bear it any longer, he followed her, determined to find out the depths of his own stupidity even though that would only deepen the pain. It was like the way a tongue would continually probe a sore tooth, in search of the pain. No matter how she tore him to shreds, he had to know, and then he would be invulnerable; no one would ever get to him again. He had once thought himself invulnerable, only to have Anna show him the chink in his emotional armor. But once he got over this, he would truly be untouchable.

Anna was calmly sitting at her desk, writing on a sheet of paper. He had expected her to be packing, at the very least, anything but sitting there scribbling away.

"What're you doing?"

She jerked a little at his harsh voice, but continued writing. Perhaps it was only that his eyes hadn't adjusted to the dimmer light, but she looked pale and drawn. He hoped savagely that she was feeling just a fraction of what he was going through right now.

"I said, what are you doing?"

She signed her name to the bottom of the page and dated it, then held it out to him. "Here," she said, using an enormous effort to keep her voice calm. "Now you won't have to worry about a paternity suit."

Saxon took the paper and turned it around to read

it. He skimmed it once, then read it again with greater attention and growing disbelief.

It was short and to the point. *I swear, of my own free will, that Saxon Malone is not the father of the child I carry. He has no legal responsibility, either to me or my child.*

She stood up and moved past him. "I'll be packed and gone by tonight."

He stared down at the paper in his hand, almost dizzy with the conflicting emotions surging back and forth inside him. He couldn't believe what she had done, or how casually she had done it. With just a few words written on a sheet of paper she had prevented herself from receiving a large sum of money, because God knew he would have paid any amount, even bankrupted himself if necessary, to make certain that baby was taken care of, not like—

He started shaking, and sweat broke out on his face. Rage welled in him again. Clutching the paper in his hand, he strode into the bedroom just as she was tugging her suitcases out of the closet.

"That's a damn lie!" he shouted, and threw the crumpled paper at her.

Anna flinched but hung on to her calm demeanor. Privately she wondered how much more she could take before she broke down and began sobbing. "Of course it's a lie," she managed as she placed the suitcases on the bed.

"That baby is mine."

She gave him an odd look. "Did you have any doubt? I wasn't admitting to being unfaithful, I was trying to give you some peace of mind."

"Peace of mind!" It seemed as if all his control had been demolished. He was shouting at her again, when in the entire three years they had known each other he had never before even raised his voice to her. "How the hell am I supposed to have any peace of mind knowing that my kid...my kid—" He stopped, unable to finish the sentence.

She began emptying her dresser drawers into the open suitcases, neatly folding and placing each garment. "Knowing that your kid—what?" she prompted.

He shoved his hands into his pockets and knotted them into fists. "Are you even going to have it?" he asked raggedly.

She went stiff, then straightened to stare at him. "What do you mean by that?"

"I mean, have you already planned an abortion?"

There was no warmth or softness at all in her brown eyes now. "Why do you ask?" she questioned evenly.

"It's a reasonable question."

He really had no idea, she thought numbly. How could he even consider the idea that she might abort his child if he had any inkling at all about the way she felt? All of the love that she had expressed during those long, dark hours might as well have been kept hidden for all the notice he'd paid it. Maybe he had just accepted her passion as the skillful act of a kept woman, designed to keep a sugar daddy happy.

But she didn't say any of that. She just looked at him for a moment before stating abruptly, "No. I'm not having an abortion," then turning back to her packing.

He made an abrupt motion with his hand. "Then what? If you're going to have it, then what are you going to do with it?"

She listened to him with growing disbelief. Had she gone crazy, or had he? What did he think she was going to do? A variety of answers occurred to her, some obvious and some not so obvious. Did he expect her to list the numerous activities involved in caring for a baby, or was he asking what her plans were? Given Saxon's usual precision of speech, always saying exactly what he meant, she was even more bewildered.

"What do you mean, 'what am I going to do with it?' What mothers usually do, I suppose."

His face was grayish and covered with a sheen of sweat. "That's my baby," he said, striding forward to catch her shoulders in his hard hands. "I'll do whatever it takes to keep you from throwing it away like a piece of garbage!"

Chapter Three

Cold chills of horror trickled down her spine, rendering her momentarily incapable of speech. All she could do was endure his tight grip on her shoulders, wide eyes fastened on him and her mouth slightly parted in disbelief. She tried several times to speak, and when she finally managed it, her voice was a hoarse croak. *"Throw it away?* Dear God! That's *sick!* Why on earth would you ever say something like that?"

He was shaking. She could feel it now, in his hands; see it in the visible tremors of his big body. His distress had the effect of relieving her own as she suddenly realized that he was upset and in need of reassurance even more, perhaps, than she was, though she didn't know why. Instinct took over and ruled her actions as she placed her hands on his chest.

"I would never do anything to harm your baby," she said gently. "Never."

His trembling intensified. His green eyes were stark with some savage emotion that she couldn't read, but he took a deep breath and locked his jaw as he fought to regain control. She saw the battle, saw what it cost him to win it, but in just a moment his hands were steady and his face, if still colorless, was as blank as rock. With great care he released her shoulders and let his hands drop to his sides.

"You don't have to leave here," he said, as if that was what they had been discussing. "It's a good apartment. You could take over the lease...."

Anna whirled away from him to hide the sharp upthrust of pain, all the more hurtful because, just for a moment, she thought he had meant that things didn't have to change. But he wasn't offering to preserve the status quo; he still intended to sever the relationship. "Don't," she said, warding off the words with a hand held back toward him. "Just... don't."

"Don't what?" he challenged. "Don't try to make it comfortable for you?"

She inhaled raggedly and let her head drop as she, in turn, tried to marshal her own control, but all she could find was weariness and a need for the truth. If this was the end, why not tell him? Pride? That was a pitiful reason for hiding something that had changed her life. She took another deep breath. "Don't ask me to stay here without you," she said. "You're the reason I'm here. Without you, I have no reason to stay." She turned and faced him, lifting her head so she could see him as she said in a clear, deliberate voice, "I love you. If I hadn't, I never would have come here at all."

Shock rippled across his face, turning it even whiter. His lips moved but made no sound.

"I planned to leave because I thought that was what you would want," she continued steadily. "You made it more than plain from the beginning that you didn't want any ties, so I didn't expect anything else. Even if you wanted to continue our—our arrangement, I don't think it's possible. I can't be a mother and continue to be your undemanding mistress, too. Babies tend to have their own priorities. So, under the present circumstances, I have to leave. That doesn't mean I'll stop loving you." *Ever,* she added in her thoughts.

He shook his head, either in disbelief or denial, and moved jerkily to sit down on the bed, where he stared unseeingly at the open suitcases.

Concern welled in her as she watched him. She had expected him to react with anger or cold retreat, but he truly seemed in shock, as if something terrible had happened. She walked over to sit beside him, her gaze fastened on his face in an effort to catch every fleeting nuance of expression. Saxon was hard enough to read when he was relaxed; his face looked like marble now.

Anna gripped her fingers tightly together. "I never expected you to act like this," she murmured. "I thought...I guess I thought you just wouldn't care."

His head jerked up, and he gave her a look like

a sword edge, sharp and slicing. "You thought I'd just walk away and never give another thought to either you or the baby?" His tone was harsh with accusation.

She didn't back down. "Yes, that's exactly what I thought. What else could I think? You've never given me any indication that I was anything more to you than a convenient sexual outlet."

His heart twisted painfully, and he had to look away. She thought she was only a convenience, when he measured his life by the time he spent with her. Not that he had ever let her know; she was right about that. He had gone out of his way to keep her from knowing. Was that why he was losing her now? He felt as if he had been shredded, but he was in too much pain to be able to tell which was hurting worse, the knowledge that he was losing her or that he had fathered a baby who was also lost to him.

"Do you have a place to go?" he asked numbly.

She sighed inaudibly, releasing the last frail grasp of hope. "No, not really, but it's okay. I've looked around a little, but I haven't wanted to commit on anything until I talked to you. I'll go to a hotel. It won't take me long to find another apartment. And you've made certain I won't be strapped financially. Thank you for that. And thank you for my baby." She managed a faint smile, but he wasn't looking at her and didn't see it.

He leaned forward and braced his elbows on his

knees, massaging his forehead with one hand. Lines of weariness were cut into his face. "You don't have to go to a hotel," he muttered. "You can look for another place from here. There's no point in moving twice. And we have a lot of legal stuff to get sorted out."

"No we don't," she said. He slanted his head to the side to give her another of those incisive looks. "We don't," she insisted. "You've made certain of my financial security. I'm more than able to provide for my baby. If you think I'm going to be bleeding you dry, you can just think again!"

He straightened. "What if I want to support it? It's my kid, too. Or didn't you plan on ever letting me see it?"

She was frankly bewildered. "Do you mean you *want* to?" She had never expected that. What she had expected was a cold and final end to their relationship.

That look of shock crossed his features once again, as if he had just realized what he'd said. He gulped and got to his feet, striding restlessly around the room. He had so much the look of a trapped animal that she took pity on him and said softly, "Never mind."

Instead of reassuring him, her words seemed to disturb him even more. He ran his hands through his hair, then turned abruptly toward the door. "I can't—I have to think things through. Stay here as long as you need.''

He was gone before she could call him back, before she truly realized he was leaving. The front door slammed even before she could get up from the bed. She stared at the empty space where he had stood, and recalled the haunted look in his eyes. She recognized that he was more deeply disturbed than she had ever considered possible, but had no clue as to why. Saxon had kept his past so completely private that she knew absolutely nothing about his childhood, not even who his parents were. If he had any family at all, she didn't know about them. But then, it didn't necessary follow that she would; after all, he still had his own apartment, and his mail still went there. Nor did she think it likely that he would have given out his mistress's telephone number so his family could contact him if he didn't answer his own phone.

She looked around at the apartment she had called home for two years. She didn't know if she would be able to stay here while she looked for someplace else, despite his generous offer. She had been telling him nothing less than the truth when she had said that she didn't want to stay here without him. The apartment was permeated with his presence, not physical reminders so much as the sharp memories that would be a long time fading. Her child had been conceived in the very bed she sat on. She thought about that for a moment; then her lips curved in a wryly gentle smile. Perhaps not; Saxon had never felt the need to limit their lovemaking to the bed, though they had usually sought it for comfort's sake. It was, she supposed, just as likely to have happened in the shower, or on the sofa, or even on the kitchen counter, one cold afternoon when he had arrived while she was cooking dinner and hadn't been inclined to wait until bedtime.

Those days of wondrous passion were over now, as she had known they would be. Even if Saxon hadn't reacted as she had anticipated, the end result was the same.

Saxon walked. He walked automatically, without aim or care. He was still reeling from the twin blows Anna had dealt him, incapable of ordering his thoughts or controlling his emotions. He had controlled every aspect of his life for so long, closing a door in his mind on the things that had happened years before, and he had thought the monster tamed, the nightmare robbed of horror. Yet all it had taken to destroy his deceptively fragile peace was the knowledge that Anna was pregnant. And she was leaving him. God, she was leaving him.

He felt like raising his fists to the sky and cursing whatever fate had done this to him, but the pain was too deep for that. He would have crouched on the sidewalk and howled like a demented animal if it would have relieved even a portion of the swelling agony in his chest and mind, but he knew it would not. The only surcease he would find would be where he had always found it: with Anna.

He couldn't even begin to think of the future. He had no future, no anchor. The image of endless days stretching before him refused to form; he simply couldn't face even one more day, let alone an eternal procession of them. A day without Anna? Why bother?

He'd never been able to tell her how much she meant to him. He could barely tolerate even admitting it to himself. Love, in his experience, was only an invitation to betrayal and rejection. If he allowed himself to love, then he was making himself vulnerable to a destruction of the mind and soul. And no one had loved him, not ever. It was a lesson he had learned from the earliest reaches of memory, and he had learned it well. His very survival had depended on the hard shell of indifference he had cultivated, so he had formed layer after layer of armor.

When had it changed from protection to prison? Did the turtle ever long for freedom from its boxy shell, so it could run unhindered? Probably not, but he wasn't so lucky. Anna had said that she loved him, and even if it wasn't true, in saying it she had given him the opportunity to stay just a little while longer, if only he had dared to take it. He hadn't, because it would have meant shedding at least a few layers of his armor, and the prospect filled him with a terror founded in earliest childhood and strengthened through long years of abuse.

When he arrived in front of his apartment door he stood staring at it in bewilderment, not quite certain of his location. When he finally realized that he was, in fact, at his own apartment, that he had walked several miles to reach it, he fumbled in his pocket for the keys.

The apartment was silent and musty when he entered, without any sweet welcoming presence. Anna had never been here, and it showed. He could barely stand to spend any time here. It was dark and empty, like a grave, and he was incapable of bringing any light into it. The only light he'd ever known had been Anna's, and he had shared it for too short a time, then driven her away with his own unbridled lust. He'd never been able to keep his hands off her. He had made love to her far more often than he ever would have thought possible, his male flesh rising again and again for the incredible sweetness of sinking into her and joining his body to hers. He had made her pregnant, and because of it he had lost her.

What would he do without her? He couldn't function, couldn't find it in himself to give a damn about contracts, or whether the job got done or not. Even when he had spent days on a job, he had always done it knowing that she was waiting for him. By working so hard, even if it took him away from her, he was able to take care of her and make certain she never had to do without anything. Every time he had expanded the stock portfolio he had set up for her, he had felt an intense satisfaction. Maybe he had thought that his diligent efforts in that would keep her with him, that they would show her that she was better off with him than with anyone else, or out on her own.

He couldn't let himself think, even for a moment, that she might have stayed with him only because he *was* establishing her financial security. If he thought that about Anna, then he truly had nothing left to live for. No, he had always known that she had disliked that part of their arrangement.

There had been no reason at all for her to stay... unless she *did* love him.

For the first time, he let himself think about what she had said. At the time, it had been too much for him to take in, but now the words circled tentatively in his consciousness, like frail birds afraid to light.

She loved him.

He sat in the silent apartment for the rest of the day and into the night, too far withdrawn into himself to feel the need for light or noise, and sometime during the dark hours he crossed an internal barrier. He felt as if he were pinning his desperate hopes on the slimmest of chances, as if he were shooting for the longest odds, but he faced the cold gray fact that he could do nothing else.

If Anna loved him, he couldn't let her go like this.

Chapter Four

Anna had a bad night. She couldn't sleep; though she hadn't expected to sleep well, neither had she expected to lie awake for hours, staring at the dark ceiling and physically aching at the empty space beside her. Saxon had spent many nights away from her before, on his numerous business trips, and she had always managed to sleep. This, however, was different, an emptiness of the soul as well as of space. She had known it would be difficult, but she hadn't known it would leave this wrenching, gnawing pain inside. Despite her best efforts, she had cried until her head had started throbbing, and even then she hadn't been able to stop.

It was sheer exhaustion that finally ended the tears, but not the pain. It was with her, unabating, through the long dark hours.

If this was what the future would be like, she didn't know if she could bear it, even with the baby. She had thought that his child, immeasurably precious, would be some consolation for his absence, and though that might be so in the future, it was a hollow comfort now. She couldn't hold her baby in her arms right now, and it would be five long months before she could.

She got up toward dawn without having slept at all, and made a pot of decaffeinated coffee. Today of all days she needed the kick of caffeine, but her pregnancy forbade it. She made the coffee anyway, hoping that the ritual would fool her brain into alertness, then sat at the kitchen table with a thick robe pulled around her for comfort while she sipped the hot liquid.

Rain trickled soundlessly down the glass terrace doors and jumped in minute splashes on the drenched stone. As fine as the day before had been, the fickle April weather had turned chilly and wet as a late cold front swept in. If Saxon had been there, they would have spent the morning in bed, snuggled in the warmth of the bed covers, lazily exploring the limits of pleasure.

She swallowed painfully, then bent her head to the table as grief welled up overwhelmingly again. Though her eyes felt grainy and raw from weeping, it seemed there were still tears, still an untapped capacity for pain.

She didn't hear the door open, but the sound of footsteps on the flagstone flooring made her jerk upright, hastily wiping her face with the heels of her hands. Saxon stood before her, his dark face bleak and drawn with weariness. He still had on the same clothes he'd worn the day before, she saw, though he had thrown on a leather bomber jacket as protection against the rain. He had evidently been walking in it, because his black hair was plastered down, and rivulets of moisture ran down his face.

"Don't cry," he said in a raw, unnatural tone.

She felt embarrassed that he had caught her weeping. She had always taken pains to hide any bouts of emotion from him, knowing that they would make him uncomfortable. Nor did she look her best, with her eyes swollen and wet, her hair still tousled from a restless night, and swaddled from neck to foot in a thick robe. A mistress should always be well-groomed, she thought wryly, and almost burst into tears again.

Without shifting his gaze from her, he took off his jacket and hung it over the back of a chair. "I didn't know if you had stayed," he said, the strain still evident in his voice. "I hoped you had, but—" Then, abruptly, he moved with that shocking speed of his, scooping her up in his arms and carrying her quickly into the bedroom.

After a small startled cry, Anna clung to his shoulders. He had moved like that the first time, as if all his passion had been swelling behind the dam of his control and the dam had finally given way. He had swept her off her feet and down to the floor in the office almost in the same motion, then had come down on top of her before her surprise could give way to gladness. She had reached for him with desire that rose quickly to match his, and it had been hours before he had released her.

She could feel the same sort of fierceness in his grip now as he placed her on the bed and bent over her, loosening the robe and spreading it wide. Beneath it she wore a thin silk nightgown, but evidently even that was too much. Silently she stared up at his intent face as he lifted her free of the robe, then tugged the nightgown over her head. Her breath quickened as she lay naked before him, and she felt her breasts tighten under his gaze, as hot as any touch. A warm, heavy pooling of sensation began low in her body.

He opened her thighs and knelt between them, visually feasting on her body as he fumbled with his belt and zipper, lowering his pants enough to free himself. Then his green gaze flashed upward to meet the drowning velvet brown of hers. "If you don't want this, say so now."

She could no more have denied him, and herself, than she could willingly have stopped breathing. She lifted her slender arms in invitation, and he leaned forward in acceptance, sheathing himself in both her body and her embrace with one movement. He groaned aloud, not just at the incredible pleasure, but at the cessation of pain. For now, with her slender body held securely beneath him, and himself held just as securely within her, there was no distance between them.

Anna twisted under the buffeting of a savagely intense sensual pleasure. The shock of his cold, damp clothing on her warm bare body made her feel more naked than she ever had before. The single point of contact of bare flesh, between her legs, made her feel more sexual, made her painfully aware of his masculinity as he moved over and inside her. It was too overwhelming to sustain, and she arched into climax too soon, far too soon, because she wanted it to last forever.

He stilled, holding himself deep inside her for her pleasure, holding her face and planting lingering kisses over it. "Don't cry," he murmured, and until then she hadn't known that there were tears seeping out of her eyes. "Don't cry. It doesn't have to end now."

She had cried it aloud, she realized, had voiced her despair at the swift peaking.

He brought all the skill and knowledge of two years of intimacy into their lovemaking, finding the rhythm that was fast enough to bring her to desire again, but slow enough to keep them from reaching satisfaction. There was a different satisfaction in the lingering strokes, in the continued linking of their bodies. Neither of them wanted it to end, because as long as they were together like this they wouldn't have to face the specter of separation. Withdrawal, right now, would mean more than the end of their lovemaking; it would be a parting that neither could bear.

His clothing became not a sensual pleasure, but

an intolerable barrier. She tore at the buttons on his shirt, wanting the wet cloth out of the way, needing the pressure of his skin on hers. He rose enough to shrug his wide shoulders out of the garment and toss it aside; then he lowered his chest, and she whimpered in delight at the rasp of his hair on her sensitive nipples.

He cupped her breasts in both hands and pushed them together, bending his head to brush light kisses over the tightly drawn nipples. They were a bit darker, he noticed, and the pale globes were a little swollen, signs of his baby growing within her flat belly. He shuddered with unexpected excitement at the thought, at the knowledge that the same act he was performing now had resulted in that small life.

He had to grit his teeth in an effort to keep from climaxing right then. His baby! It seemed that knowledge wasn't quite the same thing as realization, and he had just been hit by the full realization that the baby was his, part of him, sharing his genes. Blood of his blood, bone of his bone, mingled inseparably with Anna, a living part of both of them. He felt a wave of physical possession like he'd never known before, never even dreamed existed. His baby!

And his woman. Honey-sweet Anna, smooth warm skin and calm, gentle dark eyes.

The crest had been put off too long to be denied any longer. It swept over them, first engulfing her, then him, her inner trembling too much for him to bear. They heaved together in a paroxysm of pleasure, crying out, dying the death of self and surfacing into the quiet aftermath.

They lay entwined, neither of them willing to be the first to move and break the bond of flesh. Anna slid her fingers into his damp hair, loving the feel of his skull beneath her fingers. "Why did you come back?" she whispered. "It was hard enough watching you leave the first time. Did you have to put me through it again?"

She felt him tense against her. Before, she would never have let him know her feelings; she would have smiled and retreated into her role of the perfect mistress, never making demands. But she had left that shield behind, baring herself with her declaration of love, and there was no going back. She wasn't going to deny that love again.

He rolled to his side, taking her with him, wrapping his arm around her hip to keep her in place. She shifted automatically, lifting her leg higher around his waist for greater comfort. He moved closer to deepen his tenuous penetration, and they both breathed infinitesimal sighs of relief.

"Do you have to go?" he finally asked. "Why can't you just stay?"

She rubbed her face against his shoulder, her dark eyes sad. "Not without you. I couldn't bear it."

She felt the effort it took him to say, "What

if…what if I stay, too? What if we just go on as before?"

She lifted her head to look at him, studying his beloved features in the rain-dimmed light. She wasn't unaware of what it had taken for him to make such an offer; he had always been so diligent in shunning even the appearance of caring, yet now he was actually reaching out to her, asking for the ties of emotion. He needed to be loved more than any man she had ever seen, but she didn't know if he could tolerate it. Love brought responsibilities, obligations. It was never free, but required a high payment in the form of compromise.

"Can you?" she asked, the sadness as evident in her tone as in her eyes. "I don't doubt that you would try, but could you stay? There's no going back. Things have changed, and they'll never be the same again."

"I know," he said, and the stark look in his eyes hurt her, because she could see that he didn't really believe he could succeed.

She had never before pried into his past, just as she had never before told him that she loved him, but their insular little world had unraveled with frightening speed and turned things upside down. Sometimes, to make a gain, you had to take a risk.

"Why did you ask me if I would throw our baby away?"

The question hung in the air between them like a

sword. She felt him flinch, saw his pupils contract with shock. He would have pulled away from her then, but she tightened her leg around him and gripped his shoulder with her hand; he stopped, though he could easily have moved had he wanted to pit his strength against hers. He stayed only because he couldn't bring himself to give up her touch. She bound him with her tenderness when strength couldn't have held him.

He closed his eyes in an instinctive effort to shut out the memory, but it didn't go away, couldn't go away with Anna's question unanswered. He had never talked about it before, never wanted to talk about it. It was a wound too deep and too raw to be eased by "talking it out." He had lived with the knowledge his entire life, and he had done what he'd had to do to survive. He had closed that part of his life away. It was like tearing his guts out now to answer, but Anna deserved at least the truth.

"My mother threw me away," he finally said in a guttural tone; then his throat shut down and he couldn't say anything else. He shook his head helplessly, but his eyes were still closed, and he didn't see the look of utter horror, swiftly followed by soul-shattering compassion, on Anna's face. She watched him through a blur of tears, but she didn't dare break down and begin crying, or do anything else that would interrupt him. Instead she gently stroked his chest, offering tactile comfort rather than verbal; she sensed that words weren't adequate to the task, and in any case, if she tried to speak, she would lose her battle with her tears.

But as the silence stretched into minutes, she realized that he wasn't going to continue, perhaps couldn't continue without prompting. She swallowed and tried to regain her composure; it was an effort, but finally she was able to speak in a voice that, if not quite normal, was still soft and full of the love she felt.

"How did she throw you away? Were you abandoned, adopted...what?"

"Neither." He did twist away from her then, to lie on his back with his arm thrown up to cover his eyes. She mourned his loss, but gave him the distance he needed. Some things had to be faced alone, and perhaps this was one of them. "She threw me into the garbage when I was born. She didn't put me on the church steps or leave me at an orphanage so I could make up little stories about how much my mother had really loved me, but she had been really sick or something and had had to give me away so I'd be taken care of. All the other kids could make up stories like that, and believe them, but my mother made damn sure I was never that stupid. She dumped me into a trash can when I was a few hours old. There's not much way you can mistake an action like that for motherly love."

Anna curled into a little ball on her side, her fist

shoved into her mouth to stifle the sobs that kept welling up, her streaming eyes fastened on his face. He was talking now, and though she had wanted to know, now she had to fight the urge to clap her hand over his mouth. No one should ever have to grow up knowing about such ugliness.

"She wasn't just trying to get rid of me," he continued in an emotionless voice. "She tried to kill me. It was winter when she threw me away, and she didn't bother to wrap me in anything. I don't know exactly when my birthday is, either January third or fourth, because I was found at three-thirty in the morning, and I could have been born either late on the third or early on the fourth. I almost died of exposure anyway, and I spent over a year in the charity hospital with one problem after another. By the time I was placed in an orphanage, I was a toddler who had seen so many strangers come and go that I wouldn't have anything to do with people. I guess that's why I wasn't adopted. People want babies, infants still wrapped up in blankets, not a thin, sickly toddler who screams if they reach for him."

He swallowed and took his arm down from his eyes, which stared unseeingly upward. "I have no idea who or what my parents are. No trace of my mother was ever found. I was named after the city and county where I was found. Saxon City, Malone county. Hell of a tradition to carry on.

"After a few years I was placed in a series of

foster homes, most of them not very good. I was kicked around like a stray puppy. Social services got so desperate to place me that they left me with this one family even though I was always covered with a variety of bruises whenever the caseworker came around. It wasn't until the guy kicked in a couple of my ribs that they jerked me out of there. I was ten, I guess. They finally found a fairly good foster home for me, a couple whose own son had died. I don't know, maybe they thought I'd be able to take their son's place, but it didn't work, for them or me. They were nice, but it was in their eyes every time they looked at me that I wasn't Kenny. It was a place to live, and that was all I wanted. I made it through school, walked out and never looked back.''

Chapter Five

What he had told her explained so much about the man Saxon had become and why it was so hard for him to accept any semblance of love. If the first eighteen years of his life had taught him anything, it was that he couldn't depend on what others called love but which he'd never known himself. As he had said, there was no fooling himself with pretty stories that his mother had loved him when her actions had made it plain that she not only hadn't cared, but she had deliberately left him to die. Nor had he received any real affection from the overworked staff of the charity hospital. Children learn early; by the time he had been placed in an orphanage, he had already known that he couldn't trust anyone to take care of him, so he had retreated into himself as the only surety in his life. He had depended on no one except himself for anything.

It was a lesson that had been reinforced by his childhood, shunted from one foster home to another, meeting with abuse in some of them and fitting in at none of them. Where did an outcast learn of love? The simple, heartbreaking answer was that he didn't. He had had to rise above more than simple poverty. He had needed to surmount a total lack of the most simple human caring. When she thought of what he had accomplished with his life, she was awed by his immense willpower. How hard had he had to work to put himself through college, to earn not only an engineering degree but to finish so high in his class that he'd had his choice of jobs, and from there go on to form his own company?

After the gut-wrenching tale of his childhood, they had both been emotionally incapable of probing any deeper. By mutual consent they had gotten up and gone through the motions of a normal day, though it was anything but. The past twenty-four hours had taken a toll on both of them, and they had retreated into long period of silence, punctuated only by commonplace matters such as what they would have for lunch.

He was there. He showed no indication of leaving. She took that as a sign of hope and did no packing herself. Right now, all she asked for was his presence.

It was late afternoon on that rain-drenched day when he said flatly, "You never really answered my question this morning. Can we go on as we did before?"

She glanced at him and saw that though stress was still visible on his face, he seemed to have come to terms with it. She wasn't too certain of her own reaction, but she would rather bear the strain herself than take the risk of putting him off now at a time when that might be enough to drive him away again.

She sat down across from him, trying to marshal her thoughts. Finally she said, "For myself, I would like nothing better. It nearly killed me to lose you, and I'm not too certain I can go through that again. But I can't just think of myself. We can't just think of our own arrangement. What about the baby? At first, nothing will matter to it but Mommy and Daddy, but assuming that we stay together for years, what happens when it starts school and finds out that other mommies and daddies are married? This is Denver, not Hollywood. And though no one frowns on a couple living together, the circumstances change when a baby is involved."

He looked down at his hands and said very carefully, "How is it different if you move out? Its parents still won't be married, but you'll be trying to raise it alone. Is that supposed to be better for it? I don't know what kind of a father I'd make, but I think I'd be better than nothing."

Her lips trembled, and she fiercely bit down on them. Dear God, was she making him *beg* to be included in his child's life? She had never intended that, especially in light of what he'd told her that morning. "I think you'd be a wonderful father," she said. "I've never intended to prevent you from seeing your child. It's our living arrangement I'm not sure of."

"I am. I want you, and you…you want me." He still couldn't say that she loved him. "We don't have to do anything right now. Like you said, it'll be years before it's old enough to compare us with other parents. You still have a pregnancy to get through, and God knows I won't sleep at night if I don't know you're okay. At least stay until the baby's born. I can take care of you, go with you to those childbirth classes, be with you during delivery." Though his tone was confident, his eyes were pleading, and that was what broke down her resolve. If she pushed him away now, he might never recover.

"There's nothing I'd like better," she said huskily, and saw the lightning flash of relief in his eyes before he masked it.

"I'll move my clothes in tomorrow."

She could only blink at him in surprise. She had expected him to return to the status quo, sleeping almost every night with her but returning to his own apartment every morning to change clothes before going to work. The thought of his clothes hanging next to hers in the spacious closet made her feel both excited and a little alarmed, which was ridiculous, because she had never wanted anything as much as she had wanted a full, complete life with him. But things were changing so swiftly, and her life was already in upheaval with her pregnancy. Control of her body was slipping further from her grasp with every passing day, as the baby grew and demanded more of her. Though her early symptoms had been scant, she could now see definite changes.

She had been fighting one of those changes all day, and it was all suddenly too much. Tears welled in her eyes as she looked at him, and began to roll down her face. Instantly he was beside her, putting his arms around her and tucking her head against his shoulder. "What's wrong?" he demanded, sounding almost frantic. "Don't you want me to move in? I thought I could take care of you better."

"It isn't that," she sobbed. "Yes, it is. I'm happy, damn it! I've always wanted you to move in with me, or ask me to move in with you. But you didn't do it for my sake, you did it because of the baby!"

Saxon tilted her face up and used his thumbs to wipe away her tears. His black brows were drawn together in a scowl. "Of course I'm doing it for you," he said impatiently. "I don't know the baby. Hell, I can't even see much evidence of it yet! I don't want you to be alone any more than necessary." The scowl intensified. "Have you been to a doctor?"

She sniffed and wiped her eyes. "Yes, I didn't realize I was pregnant until I saw the doctor. I went because my last period was just spotting, and the one before that was really light. I've hardly had any symptoms at all."

"Is that normal?"

"As normal as anything else is. The doctor told me everything looked fine, that some women spotted for the first few months and some didn't, that some women had morning sickness and some didn't. All I've really noticed is that I get tired and sleepy and that I want to cry a lot."

He looked relieved. "You mean you're crying because of the baby?"

"No, I'm crying because of you!"

"Well, don't." He pulled her close and pressed a kiss to her forehead. "I don't like it when you cry."

There was no way he could know how it felt to be coddled and cuddled like that, how she had yearned for it. Love had been in short supply in her life, too, though she had never known the direct brutality Saxon had suffered. Her most cherished dreams had always been about having a home with him, just an ordinary home, with the sweet security of routine and the sure knowledge that he was coming home to her every day. In her dreams he had always held her and shown her how much he cared, while in reality he had offered her physical intimacy and an emotional desert. This sudden turnaround was so much like a dream come true that she was afraid to believe in it. Even so, she wasn't going to do anything to end it prematurely. For as long as he stayed, she intended to savor every moment.

True to his word, he moved in the next day. He didn't say anything to her about it, but a couple of phone calls, one from someone interested in leasing his other apartment and another from a utility company double-checking the address for the forwarding of his bill, made it obvious that he was completely giving up his official residence. That, more than anything, told her how serious he was about preserving their relationship.

She watched him closely for signs of edginess, because their relationship had changed in far more fundamental ways than simply that he no longer had dual residences. She had told him that she loved him, words that couldn't be erased or forgotten; by his reaction to their short estrangement, he had revealed a lot more about how much he cared than he ever had before. Though they had been physically intimate for two years, this sort of closeness was totally new to him, and she could tell that sometimes he didn't know how to act. It was almost as if he were in a foreign country where he didn't speak the language, cautiously groping his way about, unable to read the road signs.

He was increasingly curious about the baby and insisted on going with her to her next doctor's appointment, which was scheduled for only a few days after he'd moved in. When he discovered that an ultrasound photo later in her pregnancy might tell them the baby's sex, he immediately wanted to know when they would be able to do it, and how often the doctors were mistaken. Since it was the first interest he had shown in the baby's sex, she wondered if he was imagining having a son. He hadn't indicated a preference either way, and she had no decided preference, either, so they had somehow always referred to the baby as "it" rather than "he" or "she."

How would a son affect him? He would see more of himself in a boy, and it would be, in a way, a chance for him to correct the horror of his own childhood by making certain his own son never knew anything but love. In her mind's eye she saw him patiently showing a grubby, determined little boy how to swing a bat or field a pop fly. There would probably be years of attending a variety of ball games and watching with fierce pride every move the boy made. Every hit would be the best hit ever made, every catch the most stupendous, because the boy making it would be *theirs*.

Despite the dampening whispers of her common sense, she couldn't stop dreaming of a future with Saxon. One miracle had already happened: he hadn't disappeared when he'd learned of her pregnancy. She would continue hoping for another miracle.

Lying in bed that night, she nestled her head on his chest and listened to the strong, steady boom-*boom* of his heart. Her hand strayed down to her abdomen; the baby was hearing her own heart steadily pumping in the same rhythm, soothing and reassuring it just as Saxon's heartbeat soothed her. It was a wonderfully satisfying sound.

"You seemed really interested in the ultrasound," she said sleepily.

"Mmm," he grunted by way of a reply. Her head moved as she glanced up at him, though all she could see was his chin, and that not very well in the darkened room.

"Are you anxious to know what the baby is?"

He shifted restlessly. "I'd like to know, yeah. What about you? Do you have your heart set on a little girl?"

"Not really," she said, and yawned. "I just want a healthy baby, boy or girl, though it would be convenient to know ahead of time so we can have a name picked out and a nursery decorated without having to use greens or yellows."

"A nursery," he said in a faintly surprised tone. "I hadn't thought that far ahead. All I can picture is this little person about the size of a skinned rabbit, all wrapped up in a blanket. It'll stay where we put it and won't take up much space. Why does something that small need an entire room for itself?"

She grinned in the darkness. "Because otherwise the entire apartment would be cluttered with all the paraphernalia necessary for taking care of a baby. And where did you think it would sleep?"

The question startled him; then he laughed, the rare sound booming under her ear. "With us, I guess. On whichever arm you weren't using. I would say it could sleep on my chest, but I understand they aren't housebroken.''

She snickered, and he laughed again. More content than she could ever remember being in her life, she snuggled even closer. ''I imagine you want a boy. All day today I kept having daydreams about you teaching him how to play baseball.''

Saxon stiffened, his body going rigid all along her side. ''Not especially,'' he finally said in a strained voice. ''I'd really rather have a girl.''

Surprise kept her silent, particularly because she didn't know what about the question had upset him. He didn't say anything for a while, and she began to drift off to sleep, but all drowsiness left her when he said quietly, ''Maybe if it's a girl you'll love it more.''

Chapter Six

"**W**hat about your family?" he asked carefully the next morning, as if wary of treading on unstable ground. In his experience, family was something other people had and, from what he'd seen at his foster homes, it wasn't desirable. But he wanted to know more about Anna, wanted to find out all he could about her in case some day he came home to find her gone. "Have you told them that you're having a baby, or anything about me?"

"I don't have any family," she replied as she poured skim milk over her cereal. Her manner was casual, but his interest sharpened immediately.

"No family? Were you an orphan?" He had seen a lot of orphans, sad and terrified children who had lost their entire world and didn't know what to do. Maybe his situation, dire as it had been, was preferable to theirs. At least he hadn't lost someone he loved. His mother hadn't died; she had simply dumped him in the trash. Probably both she and his father were still alive somewhere, though he sincerely doubted they were together. He was more than likely the result of a short affair, at best, and more probably a one-night stand.

"Yes, but I was never in an orphanage. My

mother died when I was nine, and my dad said he couldn't take proper care of me, so he sent me to live with his half sister. To tell the truth, he simply didn't want the responsibility. From what my aunt said, he'd always been irresponsible, never holding down a job for long, spending his money in bars and chasing after other women. He died in a car accident when I was fourteen.''

"What about your aunt?" he asked, remembering the "None" she had listed beside the next-of-kin information. "Do you still see her?"

"No. She died about a year before I went to work for you, but I doubt I'd ever have seen her again anyway. It wasn't a fond relationship. She and Uncle Sid had seven kids of their own. I was just an un-welcome extra mouth to feed, especially since she had never gotten along with Dad anyway. Aunt Cora looked as if she had posed for the painting 'Amer-ican Gothic,' all prune-faced and disapproving, soured on life. There was never enough money to go around, and it was only natural that she provided for her own children first.''

Anger swelled in him as he pictured her, a thin, lost little girl with big honey eyes, standing off to the side as he had often stood, never quite a part of a family unit. That had been the better part of his childhood, but it infuriated him that Anna had been subjected to such treatment. "What about your cous-ins? Don't you ever see them, or hear from them?"

''No, we were never close. We got along as well as most children who have been thrown together, but we never had much in common. They've all moved off the farm, anyway, and I don't know where they are. I suppose I could trace them if I wanted, but there doesn't seem any point in it.''

Somehow he had never pictured Anna as being alone in the world, or of having a background in common with him. It shook him to realize that, in a different way, she had been just as deprived of nurturing as he had. She had never suffered the physical abuse, and perhaps that was why she was still able to reach out, to express her love. Even before he could remember, he had learned not to expect, or hope, or offer anything of himself, because that would leave him open to hurt. He was glad Anna hadn't known a life like that.

Even so, it couldn't have been easy for her to tell him that she loved him. Had she been braced for rejection? That was what he'd done, panicked and thrown her love back in her face. He had been terrified the next morning that she wouldn't be able to stand the sight of him after the way he'd run out on her. But she had taken him back, and thank God, she not only loved him, but she seemed to love his baby. Sometimes it seemed impossible.

''What about the foster family you stayed with?'' she asked. ''Do you ever call them, or visit?''

''No. I haven't seen them since the day after my

high-school graduation, when I packed and left, but they didn't expect me to keep in touch. I told them goodbye and thanked them, and I guess that was good enough.''

''What were their names?''

''Emmeline and Harold Bradley. They were good people. They tried, especially Harold, but there was no way they could turn me into their son. It was always there, in their eyes. I wasn't Kenny. Emmeline always seemed to resent it that her son had died but I was still alive. Neither of them ever touched me if they could prevent it. They took care of me, provided me with a place to stay, clothes, food, but there wasn't any affection there. They were relieved when I left.''

''Aren't you curious if they're still alive, or if they've moved?''

''There's no point in it. There's nothing for me there, and they wouldn't be overjoyed to see me.''

''Where did they live?''

''About eighty miles from here, in Fort Morgan.''

''But that's so close! My cousins lived in Maryland, so it's at least reasonable that we haven't kept in touch.''

He shrugged. ''I left the state when I went to college, so it wasn't exactly convenient for me to visit. I worked two jobs to pay my tuition, and that didn't leave a lot of free time.''

"But you came back to Colorado and settled in Denver."

"There's more demand for engineers in a large city."

"There are a lot of cities in this country. The point is, you're so close, but you never called them to tell them how college turned out, or that you were back in the state."

Temper edged into his voice. "No, I didn't, and I don't intend to. For God's sake, Anna, it's been fifteen years since I got out of college. They sure as hell haven't kept a candle in the window for me all this time. They knew I wouldn't be back."

She dropped the subject, but she didn't forget it. Harold and Emmeline Bradley. She committed their names to memory. Despite what Saxon thought, they had spent years raising him and were likely to be more than a little interested in what had become of him.

He left for work in silence, and returned that afternoon in the same brooding mood. She left him alone, but his silence made her quietly panic. Had her questions bothered him so much that he was considering terminating their arrangement? But he had started it by asking about her family, so he had only himself to blame. In the few days since she had told him of the baby she had become accustomed to thinking of him as more approachable, more *hers,* but suddenly she was very much aware of the wall that still surrounded him. She had knocked a few chinks out of it, but it was far from demolished.

Saxon hadn't liked all that talk about his foster family, but it had started him thinking. Unless he and Anna took steps to prevent it, this baby wouldn't have much of a family, either. He couldn't picture them having other children under their present circumstances, and to his surprise, he liked the idea of more children. He wanted them to be a family, not just live-in lovers who happened to have a baby.

He hadn't had pretty fantasies about his mother, but he had often wondered, with a child's bewildered pain, what it would be like to have a real family, to belong somewhere and have someone who loved him. It was a fantasy that hadn't lasted long under the merciless weight of reality, but he still remembered how he had imagined it, the feeling of security that was at the center of it and held everything together. He hadn't been able to picture parents, beyond tall shadowy figures that stood between him and danger. He never wanted his baby to have those kinds of fantasies; he wanted it to have the reality of a stable home.

Less than a week ago, just the idea of what he was now considering would have been enough to make him break out in a panicky sweat, but he had since learned that there were worse things. Losing Anna was worse. He hoped he never in his life had to live through another day and night like he'd endured then, because he didn't think his sanity could take it. In comparison, what he was thinking now was a snap.

Thinking it was one thing, actually putting it into words was another. He watched Anna with troubled eyes, though he knew it was useless trying to predict her answer. Behind her customary serenity she was deep and complicated, seeing more than he wanted her to see, understanding more than was comfortable. With so much of her thought processes hidden from him, he wasn't at all certain how she would react, or why. If she loved him there should be no hesitation, but that wasn't necessarily the case. She was capable of sacrificing her own happiness—assuming he could make her happy—for what she thought best for the baby.

It was strange what an impact the baby had had on their lives months prior to its birth, but he didn't regret the changes. It was frightening; he had the sense of living on the edge, where any false move could send him over, but at the same time the increased openness and intimacy he shared with Anna were, without a doubt, worth every minute of worry. He didn't think he could go back to the previous loneliness he had taken for granted, even embraced.

Still, it was a decision that racked him with nerves. In the end, he couldn't say the words that would be an offer of himself, a statement of his feelings and vulnerability; instead he threw them out couched as a suggestion. "I think we should get married."

There was nothing he could have said that would have astounded her more. Her legs went weak, and she sat down heavily. "Marriage!" she said with a mixture of disbelief and total surprise.

He wasn't pleased that the solution hadn't occurred to her. "Yes, marriage. It makes sense. We're already living together, and we're having a baby. Marriage seems the logical next step."

Anna shook her head, not in refusal but in a futile effort to clear her head. Somehow she had never expected to receive a marriage proposal couched as "the logical next step." She hadn't expected a marriage proposal, period, though she had wanted one very badly. But she had wanted him to propose for different reasons, because he loved her and couldn't live without her. She suspected that was the case, but she would never know for sure if he never told her.

It wasn't an easy decision, and she didn't rush into speech. His face was impassive as he waited for her answer, his green eyes darkened and watchful. Her answer meant a lot to him, she realized. He wanted her to say yes. She wanted to say yes. The question was whether she was willing to take the chance that he did love her and marry him on blind faith. A cautious woman wouldn't want to make a

hasty decision that would affect not only the two of
them, but their child as well. A broken marriage
inevitably left its scars on all concerned.

She had taken a leap of blind faith in quitting her
job to become his mistress, and she didn't regret it.
The two years of loving him had been the best of
her life, and she could never wish them undone.
Pregnancy altered everything, she thought with a
faint curving of her lips. She couldn't just think of
herself now; she had to think of the baby. What was
logical wasn't necessarily the best choice, even
though her heart clamored for a quick acceptance.

She looked at him, her dark eyes grave. "I love
you, you know," she said.

Once such a statement would have made his face
go blank in a refusal to hear. Now he steadily returned her gaze. "I know." The knowledge didn't
make him panic; instead he treasured it, savored it,
as the most precious gift of his life.

"I want to say yes, more than anything I've ever
wanted, but I'm afraid to. I know it was your idea
for us to stay together, and you've been wonderful,
but I'm not certain that you'll still feel the same after
the baby's born. As the old saying goes, then it be-
comes a whole new ball game. I don't want you to
feel trapped or unhappy."

He shook his head as if to forestall the answer he
sensed was coming. "There's no way to predict the
future. I know why you worry about the way I'll

react, and to tell you the truth, I'm a little scared myself, but I'm excited, too. I want this baby. I want you. Let's get married and make it official." He smiled wryly. "The baby could have Malone for a last name. The second generation of a brand-new family."

Anna took a deep breath and denied herself what she had wanted more than anything else. "I can't give you an answer now," she whispered, and saw his face tighten. "It just doesn't feel right. I want to say yes, Saxon, I want that more than anything, but I'm not certain it would be the right thing to do."

"It is," he said roughly.

"Then if it is, it will still be the right thing a month from now, or two months from now. Too much has happened too fast—the baby...you. I don't want to make the wrong decision, and I think I'm operating more on my emotions now than on brainpower."

The force of his willpower shone out of his eyes, intensely green and focused. "I can't make you say yes," he said in a slow, deep voice. "But I can keep asking. I can make love to you and take care of you until you won't be able to imagine life without me."

Her lips trembled. "I can't imagine that now."

"I don't give up, Anna. When I go after something, I don't stop until I've gotten it. I want you, and I'm going to have you."

She knew exactly what he meant. When he de-

cided something, he focused on it with a fierce tun-
nel vision that didn't let him rest until he had
achieved his objective. It was a little daunting to
think of herself as the object of that kind of determination.

He smiled then, a smile that was more than a little
predatory. "You can take that to the bank, baby."

Chapter Seven

Marriage. The thought of it hovered in her consciousness during the day and crept into her dreams at night. Several times every day she started to throw caution to the winds and tell him yes, but there was a part of her that simply wasn't ready to take such an immense step. She had been willing before to settle for being his mistress, but now she was unable to settle for being his wife; she wanted him to love her, too, and admit it to both her and himself. She might be certain that he did love her, but until he could come to terms with his feelings, she couldn't rely on that. He could say "I want you," but not "I love you."

She couldn't blame him for having difficulty with the emotion. Sometimes when she was alone she cried for him, at first a discarded infant, then a lonely, frightened toddler, and finally an abused youngster with no one he could turn to for help. No one could have endured such a childhood without emotional scarring, without losing the ability both to give and accept love. When she looked at it clearly, she saw that he had reached out to her far more than could reasonably be expected.

She didn't really expect more, but she wanted it.

She couldn't get the Bradleys out of her mind.
From what he had said, he had spent six years with
them, from the time he was twelve until he was
eighteen. Six years was a long time for them to keep
him and not feel something for him. Was it possible
that they had offered him more than duty, but at the
time he hadn't been able to see it for what it was?
And how had they felt at not hearing from him ever
again?

Surely they had worried, if they had any hint of
human warmth about them. They had raised him
from a boy to a young man, given him the only
stable home life he had ever known until Anna had
become his mistress and made a sanctuary for him
in the apartment. It was always possible that it had
been exactly as he remembered it, that losing their
son had prevented them from feeling anything for
him beyond duty and a sense of pity. Pity! He would
have hated that. If he had sensed that they pitied
him, no wonder he hadn't gone back.

But though she fretted about it for several days,
she knew that she wasn't accomplishing anything
with her worrying. If she wanted to know for certain, she would have to drive to Fort Morgan and
try to find the Bradleys. It might be a useless trip,
since nineteen years had passed; they could have
moved, or even died.

Once she made the decision to go, she felt better,
even though she knew Saxon would be adamantly

against the idea. However, she didn't intend to let his opposition stop her.

That didn't mean she intended to be sneaky about it. After dinner that night she said, "I'm going to Fort Morgan tomorrow."

He tensed, and his eyes narrowed. "Why?"

"To try to find the Bradleys."

He folded the newspaper away with an angry snap. "There's no point in it. I told you how it was. Why are you worried about it, anyway? That was nineteen years ago. It's nothing to do with us now. You didn't even know me then."

"Curiosity, partly," she answered with blunt honesty. "And what if you're wrong about the way they felt? You were young. You could have misread them. And if you were wrong, then they've spent nineteen years feeling as if they lost two sons instead of just one."

"No," he said, and from the command in his voice she knew he wasn't refuting her suggestion but issuing an order.

She lifted her brows at him, mild surprise in her eyes. "I wasn't asking permission. I was letting you know where I'd be so you wouldn't worry if you called and I wasn't here."

"I said no."

"You certainly did," she agreed. "But I'm not your mistress anymore—"

"It sure as hell felt like you were last night," he

interrupted, his eyes turning greener as anger intensified the color.

She didn't intend to argue with him. Instead she smiled, and her soft face glowed as she sent him a warm look. "That was making love." And it had been wonderful. Sex between them had always been hot and urgent, but since he had moved in with her it had taken on an added dimension, a shattering tenderness that hadn't been there before. Their lovemaking was more prolonged; it was as if, before, he had always been aware that he was going to have to get up and leave, and the knowledge had driven him. Now he was relaxed and leisurely in a way he hadn't been before, with increased pleasure as a result.

There was a flicker of tension across his face at the word "love," but it was quickly gone, with no lingering echoes.

"I'm not your mistress," she repeated. "That arrangement is over with. I'm the woman who loves you, who lives with you, who's having your baby."

He looked around at the apartment. "You may not think you're my mistress anymore," he said with soft anger, "but things look pretty much the same to me."

"Because you support me? That's your choice, not mine. I'll find a job, if it will make you feel better. I've never enjoyed being a kept woman, anyway."

"No!" He didn't like that idea at all. It had always been in the back of his mind that, if he kept her totally dependent on him, she would be less likely to leave. At the same time he had invested in stocks in her name to make certain she would be financially secure. The paradox had always made him uneasy, but he wanted her to be taken care of in case something happened to him. After all, he traveled a lot and spent a lot of time on construction sites, not the safest of places. He had also made a will a year ago, leaving everything to her. He'd never told her.

"I don't want you driving that far by yourself," he finally said, but he was grasping at straws, and he knew it.

"It's less than a two-hour drive, the weather forecast is for clear and sunny conditions tomorrow. But if you want to go with me, I can wait until the weekend," she offered.

His expression closed up at the idea. He had never been back, never wanted to go back. The Bradleys hadn't mistreated him; they had been the best of all the foster homes he'd been in. But that part of his life was over. He had shut the door on it when he'd left, and he'd spent the following years working like a slave to make himself into someone who would never again be helpless.

"They may have moved," she said, offering comfort. "I just want to know."

He made a weary gesture. "Then pick up the telephone and call information. Talk to them, if they're still there. But don't involve me in it. I don't want to talk to them. I don't want to see them. I don't want anything to do with this."

She wasn't surprised at his total rejection of the past; it was hardly the type of memory he would embrace. And she hadn't expected him to go with her.

"I don't want to talk to them over the telephone," she said. "I want to drive up there, see the house. I may not approach them at all. It depends on what I find when I get there."

She held her breath, because there was one appeal he could make that she wouldn't be able to deny. If he said, "Please don't go, for my sake," then she wouldn't go. If he actually asked for anything for himself, there was no way she could turn him down. He had been rejected so much in his life that she wouldn't add to it. But because of those prior rejections, she knew he wouldn't ask in those terms. He would never put things in the context of being a personal consideration for him. He would order, he would make objections, but he wouldn't simply ask and say, "Please don't."

He refused to talk about it anymore and got up restlessly to stand at the terrace doors and look out. Anna calmly returned to her own section of the paper, but her heart was beating fast as she realized this was the first normal domestic quarrel they had ever had. To her delight, they had disagreed, and nothing major had happened. He hadn't left, nor did he seem to expect her to leave. It was wonderful. He was already able to trust her enough that he wasn't afraid a disagreement could end their relationship.

She had worried that he would overreact to arguments, since they were part and parcel of every relationship. Normal couples had disagreements; probably even saints had disagreements. Two years ago, Saxon wouldn't have been able to tolerate such a personal discussion.

He was really trying, even though it was extraordinarily difficult for him to open up. Circumstances had forced him into revealing his past, but he hadn't tried to reestablish those protective mental walls of his. He seemed to accept that once the emotional boundaries had been crossed, he couldn't make them inviolate again.

She didn't know what she could accomplish by finding the Bradleys again. Perhaps nothing. She just wanted to see them, to get a feel for herself of what that portion of Saxon's formative years had been like. If they seemed interested, she wanted to reassure them that their foster son was alive and well, that he was successful and would soon be a father himself.

With his back still to her, Saxon asked, "Are you

afraid to marry me because of my past? Is that why you want to find the Bradleys, so you can ask them questions about me?''

"No!'' she said, horrified. "I'm not *afraid* to marry you.''

"My parents could be anything—murderers, drug users. My mother may be a prostitute. The odds are pretty good she was. There may be a history of mental illness in my background. *I'd* be afraid to marry me. But the Bradleys won't be able to tell you anything, because no one knows who my parents were.''

"I'm not concerned with your parents," she said levelly. "I know you. You're rock solid. You're honest, kind, hardworking and sexy.''

"So why won't you marry me, if I'm such a good catch?''

Good question, she thought. Maybe she was being foolish in waiting. "I don't want to rush into something that might not be right for either of us.''

"I don't want my baby to be born illegitimate.''

"Oh, Saxon.'' She gave a sad laugh. "I promise you I'll make a decision long before the baby is born.''

"But you can't promise me you'll say yes.''

"No more than you can promise me our marriage would work.''

He gave her a brief, angry look over his shoulder. "You said you love me.''

"And I do. But can you say that *you* love *me?*" she asked.

He didn't answer. Anna watched him, her eyes sad and tender. Her question could be taken in two ways. He did love her, she thought, but was incapable of actually *saying* it. Maybe he felt that as long as he didn't say the words aloud, he hadn't made the emotional commitment.

Finally he said, "Is that what it'll take for you to marry me?"

"No. It isn't a test that you have to pass."

"Isn't it?"

"No," she insisted.

"You say you won't marry me because you don't know if I can handle it, but I'm willing to try. You're the one who's resisting making a commitment."

She stared at him in frustration. He was too good at arguing, agilely taking her previous arguments and using them against her. She was glad that he felt sure enough of her to do it, but she could see what she'd be up against in the future if they did get married. It would take a lot of determination to win an argument against him.

She pointed her finger at him, even though his back was still turned and he couldn't see her. "I'm not resisting making a commitment, I'm resisting making it *now*. I think I have a right to be a little cautious."

"Not if you trust me."

That turned back was making her suspicious. She gave him a considering look, then suddenly realized he had turned his back so she wouldn't be able to read his expression. Her eyes narrowed as she realized what he was doing. He wasn't as upset or even as indignant as he sounded; he was simply using the tactic as a means of maneuvering her into agreeing to marry him. It was all part and parcel of his determination to have his way.

She got up and went over to him, wrapping her arms around his lean waist and leaning her head against his back. "It won't work," she said softly. "I'm on to you."

To her surprise, she felt his chest expand with a low laugh; then he turned within the circle of her arms and looped his own around her. "Maybe you know me too well," he muttered, but his tone was accepting.

"Or maybe you need acting lessons."

He chuckled again and rested his cheek against the top of her head. But all humor was absent from his tone a minute later when he said, "Go see the Bradleys, if you have to. There's nothing there to find out."

Chapter Eight

Fort Morgan was a small town of about ten thousand people. Anna drove around for a little while to get her bearings, then stopped at a phone booth to look up the Bradleys' address. What she would do if they weren't in the book, she didn't know. It could mean they had moved or died, or it might just mean that their number wasn't listed.

She could have asked Saxon, but she hadn't wanted to ask him for information to help her to do something of which he didn't approve. Besides, it had been nineteen years, and there was no guarantee the Bradleys would still live in the same house, even if they had remained in Fort Morgan.

The phone book wasn't very big. She flipped through it to the *B*s, then ran her finger down the column. "Bailey...Banks...Black...Boatwright... Bradley. Harold Bradley." She wrote down the address and phone number, then debated whether she should call them to get directions. She decided not to, because she wanted to catch them unawares, as it were. People could mask their true reactions if they were given warning.

So she drove to a gas station, filled up and asked directions of the attendant. Ten minutes later she

drove slowly down a residential street, checking
house numbers, and finally stopped at the curb in
front of a neat but unpretentious house. It looked as
if it had been built a good forty or fifty years before,
with an old-fashioned roofed porch across the front.
The white paint showed signs of wear but wasn't at
the point where one could definitely say the house
was in need of repainting. An assortment of potted
plants was sunning on the porch, but there weren't
any ornamentals in the small yard, which gave it a
bare look. A one-car, unconnected garage sat back
and to the side of the house.

She got out of the car, oddly reluctant now that
she was here, but she walked up the cracked sidewalk and climbed the three steps to the porch. A
porch glider, with rust spots showing where the
thick white paint had chipped, was placed in front
of the windows. Anna wondered if the Bradleys sat
out there during the summer and watched the neigh-
bors go about their business.

There wasn't a doorbell. She knocked on the
frame of the screen door and waited. A gray-and-
white cat leaped up onto the porch and meowed cu-
riously at her.

After a minute, she knocked again. This time she
heard hurried footsteps, and her pulse speeded up in
anticipation. With it came a wave of nausea that had
her swallowing in desperation. Of all the times to

have one of her rare bouts of morning sickness! She only hoped she wouldn't disgrace herself.

The door opened, and she found herself face-to-face with a tall, thin, stern-faced woman, only the thin screen separating them. The woman didn't open the screen door. Instead she said, "Yes?" in a deep, rusty-sounding voice.

Anna was dismayed by the lack of friendliness and started to ask for directions as an excuse for being there, planning to leave without ever mentioning Saxon. But the tall woman just stood there with her hand on the latch, patiently waiting for Anna to state her business before she opened the door, and something about that strength of will struck a cord.

"Mrs. Bradley?"

"Yes, I'm Mrs. Bradley."

"My name is Anna Sharp. I'm looking for the Bradleys who used to be foster parents to Saxon Malone. Is this the right family?"

The woman's regard sharpened. "It is." She still didn't unlatch the door.

Anna's hopes sank. If Saxon hadn't been exposed to any sort of love even here, where he had grown up, he might never be able to give or accept it. What sort of marriage could she have under those conditions? What would it do to her own child to have a father who always kept at a distance?

But she had come this far, so she might as well carry on. She was aware, too, of the compelling quality of the woman's steely gaze. "I know Saxon," she began, and with an abrupt movement the woman flipped the latch up and swung the screen door outward.

"You know him?" she demanded fiercely. "You know where he is?"

Anna moved back a step. "Yes, I do."

Mrs. Bradley indicated the interior of the house with a jerk of her head. "Come inside."

Anna did, cautiously, obeying an invitation that had sounded more like a command. The door opened directly into the living room; a quick look around told her that the furniture was old and threadbare in spots, but the small room was spotless.

"Sit," said Mrs. Bradley.

She sat. Mrs. Bradley carefully relatched the screen door, then wiped her hands on the apron she wore. Anna watched the motion of those strong, work-worn hands, then realized that it was more of a nervous wringing than it was a deliberate movement.

She looked up at her reluctant hostess's face and was startled to see the strong, spare features twisted in a spasm of emotion. Mrs. Bradley tried to school herself, but abruptly a lone tear rolled down her gaunt cheek. She sat down heavily in a rocker and bunched the apron in her hands. "How is my boy?" she asked in a broken voice. "Is he all right?"

* * *

They sat at the kitchen table, with Mrs. Bradley drinking coffee while Anna contented herself with a glass of water. Mrs. Bradley was composed now, though she occasionally dabbed at her eyes with the edge of the apron.

"Tell me about him," Emmeline Bradley said. Her faded blue eyes were alight with a mixture of joy and eagerness, and also a hint of pain.

"He's an engineer," Anna said, and saw pride join the other emotions. "He owns his own company, and he's very successful."

"I always knew he would be. Smart! Lordy, that boy was smart. Me and Harold, we always told each other, he's got a good head on his shoulders. He always got A's in school. He was dead serious about his schooling."

"He put himself through college and graduated near the top of his class. He could have gone to work with any of the big engineering firms, but he wanted to have his own business. I was his secretary for a while."

"Fancy that, his own secretary. But when he made up his mind to do something, he done it, even when he was just a boy."

"He's still like that," Anna said, and laughed. "He says exactly what he means and means exactly what he says. You always know where you stand with Saxon."

"He didn't talk much when he was here, but we

understood. The child had been through so much, it was a wonder he'd talk at all. We tried not to crowd him, or force ourselves on him. It about broke our hearts sometimes, the way he would jump to do every little thing we mentioned, then kinda hold himself off and watch to see if we thought he'd done it right. I guess he thought we were going to throw him out if he didn't do everything perfect, or maybe even kick him around the way they'd done in some of those other homes.''

Tears welled in Anna's eyes, because she could see him all too plainly, young and thin and still helpless, his green eyes watchful, empty of hope.

''Don't cry,'' Emmeline said briskly, then had to dab at her own eyes. ''He was twelve when we got him, bone-thin and gangly. He hadn't started getting his height yet, and he was still limping where the woman who had him before us knocked him off the porch with a broom handle. He twisted his ankle pretty bad. He had some long, thin bruises across his back, like the broom handle had caught him there, too. I guess it was a regular thing. And there was a burn mark on his arm. Mind you, he never said anything about it, but the caseworker told us a man ground out his cigarette on him.

''He never acted scared of us, but for a long time he'd get real stiff if we got too close to him, like he was getting ready to either fight or run. He seemed more comfortable if we stayed at a distance, so we did, even though I wanted to hug him close and tell him no one was ever going to hurt him again. But he was kinda like a dog that's been beat. He'd lost his trust of people.''

Anna's throat was tight when she spoke. ''He's still distant, to some extent. He isn't comfortable with emotion, though he's getting better.''

''You know him real well? You said you used to be his secretary. Don't you still work for him?''

''No, I haven't worked for him for two years.'' A faint blush stained her cheeks. ''We're having a baby, and he's asked me to marry him.''

The color of Emmeline's eyes was faded, but her vision was still sharp. She gave Anna a piercing once-over. ''In my day we did things in reverse order, but times change. There's no shame in loving someone. A baby, huh? When's it due? I reckon this is as close to a grandchild as I'll get.''

''September. We live in Denver, so we aren't that far away. It'll be easy to visit.''

A sad look crept over Emmeline's lined face. ''We always figured Saxon didn't want to have nothing to do with us again. He said goodbye when he graduated from high school, and we could tell he meant it. Can't blame him, really. By the time we got him, his growing-up years had marked him so deep we knew he wouldn't want to think about any foster home. The caseworker told us all about him. The woman who gave birth to that boy has a lot to answer for, what she did to him and the living hell she caused his life to be. I swear, if anyone had ever found out who she was, I'd have hunted her down and done violence to her.''

"I've had the same thought myself," Anna said grimly, and for a moment her velvet brown eyes didn't look so soft.

"My Harold died several years back," Emmeline said, and nodded in acknowledgment of Anna's murmur of sympathy. "I wish he could be here now, to hear how well Saxon's turned out, but I guess he knows anyway."

Her rough, simple faith was more touching than any elaborate protestation could have been. Anna found herself smiling, because there was something joyous in Emmeline's surety.

"Saxon said you lost your own son," she said, hoping she wasn't bringing up a source of grief that was still fresh. Losing a child was something a parent should never have to experience.

Emmeline nodded, a faraway expression coming over her face. "Kenny," she said. "Lordy, it's been thirty years now since he took sick that last time. He was sickly from birth. It was his heart, and back then they couldn't do the things they can now. The doctors told us from the time he was a baby that we wouldn't get to keep him all that long, but somehow knowing don't always help you prepare for it. He died when he was ten, poor little mite, and he looked about the size of a six-year-old.''

After a minute the dreamy expression left her face, and she smiled. ''Saxon, now, you could tell right off, even as thin and bruised up as he was, he was a strong one. He started growing the next year after we got him. Maybe it was having regular meals that did it. Lord knows I poked all the food down him I could. But he shot up like a bean pole, growing a foot in about six months. Seemed like every time we got him some jeans, he outgrew them the next week. He was taller than Harold in no time, all legs and arms. Then he started to fill out, and that was a sight to behold. All of a sudden we had more young gals walking up and down the street than I'd ever imagined lived within a square mile of this house, giggling to each other and watching the door and windows, trying to get a glimpse of him.''

Anna laughed out loud. ''How did he take being the center of attention like that?''

''He never let on like he noticed. Like I said, he was real serious about his schooling. And he was still leery about letting folks get close to him, so I guess dating would have been uncomfortable for him. But those girls just kept walking past, and can't say as I blame them. He made most boys his age look like pipsqueaks. He was shaving by the time he was fifteen, and he had a real beard, not a few scraggly hairs like most boys. His chest and shoulders had gotten broad, and he was muscled up real nice. Fine figure of a boy.''

Anna hesitated, then decided to touch on the subject of Kenny again. Emmeline tended to get carried away talking about Saxon, perhaps because she had been denied the privilege for so many years. Now that she had finally met somebody who knew him, all the memories were bubbling out.

''Saxon told me that he always felt you resented him because he wasn't Kenny.''

Emmeline gave her a surprised look. ''Resented him? It wasn't his fault Kenny died. Let me tell you, you don't ever get over it when your child dies, but Kenny had been dead for several years before we got Saxon. We'd always planned to either adopt or take in foster kids, anyway, after Kenny left us. Kenny's memory laid a little easier after Saxon came to live with us. It was like he was happy we had someone else to care about, and having Saxon kept us from brooding. How could we resent him, when he'd been through such hell? Kenny didn't have good health, but he always knew we loved him, and even though he died so young, in some ways he was luckier than Saxon.''

''He needs to be loved so much,'' Anna said, her throat tightening again. ''But it's so hard for him to reach out to anyone, or let anyone reach out to him.''

Emmeline nodded. ''I guess we should have tried

harder, after he'd had time to realize we weren't going to hurt him, but by then we were kinda used to keeping our distance from him. He seemed more comfortable that way, and we didn't push him. Looking back, I can see what we should've done, but at the time we did what it seemed like he wanted." She sat for a minute in silence, rocking back and forth a little in the wooden kitchen chair. Then she said, "Resent him? Never for a minute. Land sakes, we loved him from the beginning."

Chapter Nine

Saxon's face tightened when she told him Harold was dead, and the brilliant color of his eyes dimmed. She had expected him to refuse to listen to anything about the Bradleys, but he hadn't. If he was curious, though, he was hiding it well, because he hadn't asked any questions, either. The news of Harold's death jolted him into showing interest, though reluctantly. "Emmeline is still living in the same old house by herself?"

She told him the address, and he nodded. "It's the same house."

"She seems to be in good health," Anna said. "She cried when I told her I knew you." She took a deep breath. "You should go see her."

"No," he said shortly, dismissing the idea with a frown.

"Why not?"

She could feel him withdrawing, see his face closing up. She reached out and took his hand, remembering what Emmeline had said about letting him pull away when they should have pulled him closer. "I won't let you shut me out," she said. "I love you, and we're in this together."

His eyes were unreadable, but she had his attention. "If I had a problem, would you want to help me, or would you leave me to deal with it on my own?" she pressed.

There was a flicker of expression, gone too fast for her to decipher. "I'd take care of it for you," he said, and his hand tightened on hers. "But I don't have a problem."

"Well, I think you do."

"And you're determined to help me with it whether I think it exists or not, is that it?"

"That's it. That's the way relationships work. People butt in on other people's business because they care."

Once he would have thought it was an intolerable encroachment on his privacy, but though her determination was irritating him, at the same time it made him feel oddly secure. She was right; this was the way relationships worked. He'd seen it, though this was the first time he'd experienced it. Somehow their "arrangement" had become a "relationship," full of complications, demands and obligations, but he wouldn't have chosen to go back. For the first time in his life he felt accepted as he really was; Anna knew all there was to know about him, all the hideous details of his birth and childhood. She knew the worst, yet she hadn't left.

On a sudden impulse he lifted her astride his lap so he could look full into her face while they talked. It was an intensely personal position for talking, both physically and mentally, but it felt right. "It wasn't a good time of my life," he said in an effort to explain. "I don't want to remember it, or revisit it."

"The way you remember it is distorted by everything that had gone before. You think of them as cold and resentful of you because you weren't their son, but that isn't at all the way they felt."

"Anna," he said patiently, "I was there."

She framed his face with her hands. "You were a frightened boy. Don't you think it's possible you were so used to rejection that you expected it, so that's what you saw?"

"So you're an amateur psychiatrist now?"

"Reasoning doesn't require a degree." She leaned forward and stole a quick kiss. "She talked for hours, telling me all about you."

"And now you think you're an expert."

"I *am* an expert on you," she snapped. "I've studied you for years, from the minute I went to work for you."

"You're pretty when you're mad," he said, abruptly enjoying this conversation. He realized with surprise that he was teasing her, and that it was fun. He could make her angry, but she would still love him anyway. Commitment had its advantages.

"Then I'm about to get a lot prettier," she warned.

"I can handle it."

"You think so, big guy?"

"Yes, ma'am." He cupped his hands on her hips and moved her suggestively. "I'm pretty sure I can."

For a moment her eyelids drooped heavily in response; then she opened her eyes wide and glared at him. "Don't try to distract me."

"I wasn't trying."

No, he was accomplishing, without effort. She was far from finished with her efforts to convince him, though, so she started to get up. His hands tightened on her hips and kept her in place. "Stay right where you are," he ordered.

"We can't talk in this position. You'll get your mind on sex, and then where will we be?"

"Probably right here on this couch. Not for the first time, either."

"Saxon, would you please be serious about this?" she wailed, then stopped in astonishment at what she had just said. She couldn't believe she had just had to plead with him to be serious. He was the most sober of men, seldom laughing or even smiling. She had probably seen him smile more in the past week or so than in the rest of the three years she had known him.

"I *am* serious," he said. "About this position, and about Emmeline. I don't want to go back. I don't want to remember."

"She loves you. She called you 'her boy,' and she said that our baby would be her grandchild."

He frowned a little, his attention caught. "She said that?"

"You should talk to her. Your memory is one-sided. They understood that you were wary of adults getting close to you, after the abuse you'd received, and that's why they didn't try to touch you. They thought they were making it easier on you."

A stark look came into his eyes as memories surfaced.

"Did you want them to hug you?" she asked. "Would you have let them?"

"No," he said slowly. "I couldn't have stood it. Even when I started having sex, in college, I didn't want the girl to put her arms around me. It wasn't until—" He broke off, his eyes unfocused. It wasn't until Anna that he had wanted the feel of arms around him, that he had wanted her to hold him close. With all the other women, he had held their hands above their heads, or he had been up on his knees out of their reach. But that had been sex; with Anna, from the very beginning, it had been making love, only it had taken him two long years to realize it.

He would never have allowed Emmeline or Harold to hug him, and they had known it.

Had his perceptions, and therefore his memories, been so distorted by his previous experiences? If what he had seen had been reflections in the carnival mirror of his mind, then nothing was as it had seemed. The beatings and general abuse he had suffered at the other foster homes had trained him to expect rejection, and he had been too young to be analytical.

"Can you really get on with your life unless you know for sure?" she asked, leaning closer to him. Those honey-dark eyes were pools he could drown in, and suddenly he pulled her tight against his chest.

"I'm trying to get on with my life," he muttered against her hair. "I'm trying to build a life, with you. Let the past go. God knows I've spent enough years trying to do that, and now that it's working, why dig it up again?"

"Because you can't let go of it! You can't forget your past. It's part of what made you the man you are. And Emmeline loves you. This isn't all for your sake. Part of it is for hers. She's alone in the world now. She didn't whine about it, or complain because you'd been gone for nearly twenty years and had never been back to see her. She just wanted to know if you were all right, and she was so proud to hear how well you've done."

Saxon closed his eyes, fighting to keep the images from forming in his mind, but it was a useless battle. Emmeline had always been the stronger personality; Harold had been softer, gentler. He could still see her face, strong-boned, plain, as spare as a desert landscape. Never malevolent, but stern and upright. Her standards of cleanliness had been of the highest; for the first time in his life, he had always had good, clean clothes, clothes he hadn't been ashamed to go to school in.

He didn't want to think that she had spent twenty years wondering about him, worrying. No one had ever worried about him before, so the possibility simply hadn't occurred to him. All he had thought about was making a clean break with his past, making something of himself and never looking back.

Anna thought you had to look back, to see where you had been, as if the landscape changed once you had passed it. And maybe it did. Maybe it would look different now.

From habit he thrust emotion away from him, and the logic of the thing was suddenly clear to him. He didn't want to go back. He wanted Anna to marry him. Anna wanted him to go back. The three ideas fell into place, and all at once he knew what he would do.

"I'll go back," he said softly, and her head jerked up, her doe-eyes big and soft and questioning. "On one condition."

They faced each other in silence for a moment. He remembered the beginning of their relationship, when she had said she would be his mistress on one condition, and he had refused it, forcing her to take him on his terms. She was remembering, too, and he wondered if she would refuse on principle. No, not Anna. She was infinitely forgiving, and wise enough to know that the one instance had nothing to do with the other. He also accepted that he wouldn't always win, but that was okay, as long as Anna was the victor. As long as she won, he won, too.

"So let's hear it," she said, though she already knew. "What's the condition?"

"That you agree to marry me."

"You'd reduce our marriage to a condition that has to be met?"

"I'll do whatever it takes, use whatever argument I have to. I can't lose you, Anna. You know that."

"You aren't losing me."

"I want it signed and sealed, on record in the county courthouse. I want you to be my wife, and I want to be your husband. I want to be a father to our kids." He gave her a crooked smile. "This is kind of like a way for me to make up for my own lousy childhood, to give my kids something better and have a real childhood through them."

Of all the things he could have said, that one got to her fast and hard. She hid her face against his neck so he wouldn't see the tears welling up in her eyes and swallowed several times so she would be able to speak normally. "All right," she said. "You have yourself a wife."

* * *

They couldn't go to Fort Morgan immediately, because of his business commitments. Looking at the calendar, Anna smiled and made plans for them to go the following Sunday, and called Emmeline to let her know. It wasn't in Emmeline's character for her to bubble over with enthusiasm, but Anna could hear the pure joy in her voice.

The day finally came. As they made the drive, Saxon could feel himself tensing. He had been in foster homes all over the state, but he had lived in Fort Morgan the longest, so he had more memories of it. He could picture every room in that old house, every piece of furniture, every photograph and book. He could see Emmeline in the kitchen, dark hair pulled tightly back in a no-nonsense bun, a spotless apron protecting her plain housedress, while mouth-watering smells from the stove filled the entire house. He remembered that she had made an apple pie that was almost sinful, rich with butter and cinnamon. He would have gorged himself on that pie if he hadn't always been wary of anything he liked being taken away, so he had always restricted himself to one slice and forced himself not to show any enthusiasm. He remembered that Emmeline had baked a lot of apple pies.

He drove to the house without any difficulty, its location permanently etched in his mind. When he parked at the curb, his chest tightened until he felt almost suffocated. It was like being caught in a time warp, stepping back almost twenty years and finding nothing had changed. There *were* changes, of course; the porch roof was sagging a little, and the cars parked in the street were twenty years newer. But the house was still white, and the undecorated lawn was still as neat as a hatbox. And Emmeline, stepping out on the porch, was still tall and thin, and her gaunt face was still set in naturally stern lines.

He opened the car door and got out. Without waiting for him to come around, Anna had climbed out on her side, but she made no move to walk forward and join him.

Suddenly he couldn't move. Not another step. With only the small expanse of lawn separating them, he looked at the woman he hadn't seen in two decades. She was the only mother he'd ever known. His chest hurt, and he could barely breathe. He hadn't known it would be like this, that he would suddenly feel like that terrified twelve-year boy again, brought here for the first time, hoping it would be better than the others, expecting more of the same abuse. Emmeline had come out on the porch then, too, and he had looked up at that stern face and felt only the old rejection and fear. He had wanted acceptance, wanted it so much that his heart had been pounding in his chest and he had been afraid he would disgrace himself by wetting his pants, but he hadn't let himself show it, because not having it at all was easier than facing another rejection. So he had closed himself off, protecting himself in the only way he knew.

Emmeline moved toward the steps. She wasn't wearing an apron; she had dressed up in one of her Sunday dresses, but she was wiping her hands on the skirt out of habit. She stopped and stared at the tall, powerful man who was still standing at the curb. It was Saxon, without a doubt. He had turned into a breathtaking man, but she had always known he would, with that olive-toned skin, black hair and eyes like the clearest emeralds. She could see his eyes now, and the expression in them was the same as it had been twenty-five years ago when the caseworker had brought him to them, scared and desperate, and needing to be loved so much it had wrung her heart. He wouldn't come any closer, she knew. He wouldn't have back then, either, except for the caseworker's grip on his arm. Emmeline had remained on the porch rather than frighten him by rushing at him. And maybe it had been a mistake, waiting for him to be brought to her. Saxon needed for people to reach out to him, because he didn't know how to make the first move.

Slowly her face relaxed into a smile. Then Emmeline, that stern, reserved woman, walked down the steps to meet her son, her mouth trembling and tears running down her cheeks, her arms outstretched. And she never stopped smiling.

Something broke inside him with an audible snap,

and he broke, too. He hadn't cried since he'd been
an infant, but Emmeline was the only anchor he had
ever had in his life, until he'd met Anna. With two
long strides he met her in the middle of the sidewalk, caught her in his arms, and Saxon Malone
cried. Emmeline put her arms around him and
hugged him as tight as she could, as if she would
never let go, and she kept saying, "My boy! My
boy!" In the middle of his tears he reached out to
Anna, and she flew around the car and into his arms.
He held them both tight in his embrace and rocked
them together, the two women he loved.

It was the twelfth of May. Mother's Day.

Epilogue

Anna woke slowly from what seemed like the deepest sleep she'd ever had and opened her eyes. The first sight she saw kept her from moving for a long, long time, as she reveled in the piercing sweetness of it. Saxon was sitting beside her hospital bed, just as he had been beside her all during labor and delivery. She had seen his face taut with worry and torment over her pain, filled with jubilation when she finally gave birth, his green eyes brilliant with tears as he stared wordlessly at his tiny, squalling offspring.

He held the sleeping baby in his arms now, all his attention focused on the little creature. With infinite care he examined the tiny, perfect hands and minuscule fingernails, almost holding his breath as the little fingers folded over his big one in a surprisingly tight reflexive grip, even in sleep. He traced a finger over the almost invisible eyebrows, down the downy soft cheek, to the pink bud of a mouth. Their son fit almost perfectly in his big hands, though he had weighed in at a respectable seven pounds.

She eased around onto her side, smiling at Saxon

when he snapped his attention to her. "Isn't he gorgeous?" she whispered.

"He's the most perfect thing I've ever seen." Awe was in his tone. "Emmeline has gone down to the cafeteria to get something to eat. I practically had to fight her to get him away from her."

"Well, he is her only grandchild. For now."

He looked incredulous, remembering her labor, but then he looked at the baby in his arms and understood how she could consider the result as being well worth the effort. Then he smiled at his wife, a slow smile that melted her bones. "As long as the next one is a girl."

"We'll try our best."

"We still haven't decided on a name for him," he said.

"You can pick out his first name. I've already decided on his middle name."

"What is it?"

"Saxon, of course," she said. "The second Saxon Malone. We're starting a new family tradition, remember?"

He reached out and took her hand, then eased himself onto the side of her bed, and together they admired their son.

*   *   *   *   *

Linda Howard

I'm a Southerner, which means I haven't strayed far from my roots. Families here tend to stay in the same area for generations, and my family is no different. Not that I don't travel, sometimes more than I like, but "home" always means the mountains and lakes of northeast Alabama. I've lived in or near Gadsden, Alabama, all of my life, usually near rather than in. I prefer rural life over city life, silence over noise solitude over crowds.

I'm the second oldest of six children, one of the two "quiet" ones (that's quiet for our family, not someone else's quiet), though my friends and family will swear I'm anything but. Let's just say that I bide my time around strangers, watching instead of talking. Looking back, I have to say that I had a wonderful childhood, as only childhood in the country can be.

I attended a rural school in Walnut Grove, then the local community college, where I was the sole journalism student in the entire college, but I saw right away that journalism wasn't for me. Those people wanted *facts*, I wanted to make up stuff. Saying goodbye to journalism, I dropped out of college and began work at a trucking company, a job that I loved because no two days were the same and the people I worked with were great.

Let's see, is there anything else of interest? I married young, divorced young and made a much more sensible choice the second time around. Gary and I have been married now for twenty-four years. He gave me three stepchildren whom I love, and who in turn gave me three grandsons. Gary fishes the Bassmaster professional tournament trail, and I usually travel with him to his tournaments.

We live on a two-hundred-acre farm, complete with

cattle, fish pond, and assorted wildlife, including bear and a black panther that I saw myself, standing in my front yard as if he owned it. Well, maybe he did. We are the servants of two dogs, one a golden retriever mix, and the other a purebred golden. For those of you who also own goldens, you know what I'm talking about. Sweeter, funnier, more loving, good-natured animals do not exist— assuming you survive their puppyhood, when they resemble perpetual motion machines!

I like a lot of sports, but I *love* football. I can't stand the look, smell, taste or touch of mayonnaise, because I had a traumatic experience with mayo when I was six. I detest the colours yellow and orange, I used to fish but stopped when Gary began tournament fishing (one in the family is enough), and I function better under a strict schedule. My musical taste ranges from classical to country, but skips over rap and jazz. I love cappuccino, specifically french vanilla. I like rainy days if I can stay home, curled up with a book. I cook, I do laundry, I run errands. All in all, it's a fairly normal life—right?

Other novels by Linda Howard

Silhouette Sensation®

Against the Rules
Tears of the Renegade
Diamond Bay
Heartbreaker
Mackenzie's Mountain
Duncan's Bride
Mackenzie's Mission
Loving Evangeline
Mackenzie's Pleasure

Silhouette Special Edition®

All That Glitters
An Independent Wife
Come Lie with Me
Sarah's Child
The Cutting Edge
Almost Forever
White Lies

Silhouette Christmas Stories 1989
"Bluebird Winter"

Silhouette Summer Sizzlers 1994
"Overload"

SINGLE LETTER SWITCH

Here's a fun puzzle for you to try!

There are two five letter words provided in the grid. The first one being STOCK, the other PLATE. All you have to do is write down the words that are missing by changing just one letter at a time to form a new word and eventually change the word STOCK into PLATE. You only have eight chances but we have supplied you with clues as to what each one is. Good Luck!

When you have found all six missing words, check your answers at the bottom of the page.

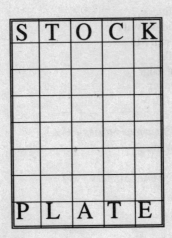

Clues:

A   To pile up
B   To ease off or a reduction
C   A dark colour
D   Empty or missing
E   A piece of wood
F   Common abbreviation for an aircraft

TESS GERRITSEN

WHISTLEBLOWER

He emerged from the mist, right in front of
Cathy Weaver's car—running from killers who
were closing in. Victor Holland's story sounded
like the ravings of a man on the brink of
madness, but his claim to be a fugitive was
confirmed by the haunted look in his eyes
—and the bullet hole in his shoulder.

As each hour brought pursuers ever
closer, Cathy had to wonder: Was she
giving her trust to a man in danger
…or trusting her life to a dangerous man?

**Available from the Reader Service™
from June 1999**

Jennifer
BLAKE

LUKE

Luke Benedict figures he's the only one in
Turn-Coupe, Louisiana, who can save novelist
April Halstead from someone intent on revenge.
If only he could get April to cooperate.

Down in Louisiana, a man'll do whatever it takes…

Available from 21st May

KAREN HARPER

Liberty's Lady

On the eve of the Revolutionary War, one woman is about to betray her own heart... by falling in love with her sworn enemy.

Spirited journalist Libby Morgan uses her newspaper to fan the flames of revolt against England. Cameron Grant, New York aristocrat, avowed Tory and secret spy, is the prime target of her blazing rhetoric. Sworn enemies by their divided loyalties, they are irresistibly drawn into a passion that does not recognize sides. Soon they are risking their lives and their love in a daring masquerade that could end in liberty—or death.

Karen Harper "has the rare talent of creating vivid history and characters, and bringing both to life."
—Romantic Times

MIRA®

Available from the Reader Service™ from May 1999

WORD LINK

There are ten words missing from our list. Each of the missing words must link up with the two on either side to make a new word or words.

For example, 'Business' links with 'Suit' and 'Case' to form 'Business Suit' and 'Suit Case':

BUSINESS—SUIT—CASE

As you find each one, write it in the space provided. When you have linked up all the words, check your answers with those on the bottom of the page.

BUSINESS	**SUIT**	CASE
BOTTLE	_____	HAT
FRONT	_____	BELL
PARTY	_____	BOX
SHOE	_____	PIPE
RAIN	_____	TIE
ARM	_____	MAN
SIDE	_____	ROOM
BEACH	_____	GOWN
FOOT	_____	KIND
BIRTHDAY	_____	BOARD

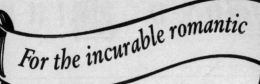

For the spirited lover in you...

Presents™

Passionate, compelling, provocative romances you'll never want to end.

Eight brand new titles each month

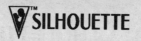

Reader Service™

The best romantic fiction direct to your door

Our guarantee to you...

The Reader Service involves you in no obligation to purchase, and is truly a service to you!

Your books are delivered hot off the press, at least one month before they are available in the shops.

Your books are sent on 14 days no obligation home approval.

We offer free postage and packing for subscribers in the UK—we guarantee you won't find any hidden extras.

Plus, we have a dedicated Customer Care team on hand to answer all your queries on
(UK) 0181 288 2888
(Ireland) 01 278 2062.
There is also a 24 hour message facility on this number.